The Dreaming

caitlin R. KIERNAN
peter HOGAN
jeff NICHOLSON
writers

peter DOHERTY   paul LEE
jeff NICHOLSON   gary AMARO
chris WESTON   d'ISRAELI
Illustrators

daniel VOZZO
Colorist

todd KLEIN
Letterer

neil GAIMAN
Consultant

THE DREAMING
created by
Neil Gaiman

Through the Gates of
HORN and IVORY

*jenette*KAHN
president & editor-in-chief

*paul*LEVITZ
executive vice president & publisher

*karen*BERGER
executive editor

*alisa*KWITNEY
editor-original series

*jim*SPIVEY
editor-collected edition

*jennifer*LEE
assistant editor-original series

*georg*BREWER
design director

*robbin*BROSTERMAN
art director

*richard*BRUNING
vp-creative director

*patrick*CALDON
vp-finance & operations

*dorothy*CROUCH
vp-licensed publishing

*terri*CUNNINGHAM
vp-managing editor

*joel*EHRLICH
senior vp-advertising & promotions

*lillian*LASERSON
vp & general counsel

*jim*LEE
editorial director-wildstorm

*john*NEE
vp & general manager-wildstorm

*bob*WAYNE
vp-direct sales

THE DREAMING:
THROUGH THE GATES OF HORN AND IVORY

DC Comics, 1700 Broadway, New York, NY 10019
A division of Warner Bros. -
A Time Warner Entertainment Company
Printed in Canada. First Printing.
ISBN: 1-56389-493-9
Cover illustration by Dave McKean.
Publication design by Jason Lyons.

ALL RIGHT, YOU DITHERING DILETTANTE, MAKE UP YOUR MIND. EITHER TAKE THE BOOK TO THE CASHIER AND PURCHASE IT, OR STOP PAWING AT IT BEFORE YOU LEAVE YOUR CLAMMY FINGERPRINTS ALL OVER THE NICE ARTWORK.

THAT'S RIGHT, I SAID PUT IT DOWN. GO **ON** BELIEVING WHAT THE NICE TELEVISION SHRINKS TELL YOU— THAT DREAMS ARE JUST YOUR SUBCONSCIOUS LETTING YOU KNOW THAT, DEEP DOWN, YOUR UNFINISHED BUSINESS WITH YOUR BEST FRIEND FEELS LIKE A WHITE MOUSE LURKING UNDER THE BED.

BALDERDASH. SOME DREAMS ARE OLDER THAN OTHERS AND CARRY THE WEIGHT OF CENTURIES. YOUR GRANDMOTHER MIGHT RECALL THAT A MOUSE UNDER YOUR BED COULD BE AN OMEN OF ILLNESS, DEATH OR WAR; OR IT MIGHT EVEN BE YOUR OWN SOUL, WANDERING ABROAD.

OR ARE YOU ONE OF THOSE RIDICULOUS MODERN SOLIPSISTS WITH OPINIONS ABOUT WINE AND CHEESE AND THE MISTAKEN BELIEF THAT YOUR DREAMS ARE YOURS ALONE? WELL, WAKE UP AND SMELL THE CURDLED BLOOD, I SAY. DREAMS THAT HAVE BEEN DREAMT OFTEN ENOUGH MAY EVEN VENTURE OUT BEYOND THE GATES OF HORN AND IVORY AND WIND UP SHARPENING THEIR TEETH ON YOUR BEDPOST.

AND SOMETIMES, EVEN A DREAM MAY DREAM, WITH STARTLING CONSEQUENCES. YOU SEE, THE DREAMING IS A REALM WHERE A SINGLE STEP OFF THE PATH MAY CAUSE A VISITOR TO MEET HIS NEMESIS; WHERE A RAVEN MAY INSTRUCT YOU IN COVERT OPERATIONS, AND WHERE AN IRRITATINGLY OUTSPOKEN PUMPKIN CAN UNDO THE TEACHINGS OF A LIFETIME. AND, ABOVE ALL, THE DREAMING IS A PLACE OF MYSTERIES AND SECRETS.

BUT YOU CAN DISCOVER ALL THIS FOR YOURSELF. AND PROBABLY WILL, IF YOU'VE MANAGED TO READ THIS FAR...WITHOUT FALLING ASLEEP.

Cain

CARETAKER OF THE HOUSE OF MYSTERY

"Day's Work, Night's Rest"

DAY'S WORK, NIGHT'S REST

EVEN IF IT'S ONLY NINE FORTY-FIVE IN THE MORNING, ALL I WANT TO DO IS CRAWL BACK INTO BED AND SLEEP. BUT I DON'T, BECAUSE I WOULD EVENTUALLY HAVE TO WAKE UP AND RETURN. THE OFFICE WINS. MY BED LOSES.

YOU THINK THAT'S NORMAL, DON'T YOU? YOU SAY YOU FEEL THAT WAY EVERY SINGLE DAY, BUT I'M DIFFERENT. I'M RE-SPONSIBLE. I *OWN* THIS PLACE.

YES, I CONCEIVED OF THIS PLACE. I DREAMED IT UP AND HAD IT BUILT, FOR LACK OF SOMETHING BETTER TO DO. IT SHOULD BE STIMULATING. BUT IT FEELS EXACTLY THE SAME AS SITTING IN A MORNING CLASS IN COLLEGE. A SLEEPY STRESS.

JEFF NICHOLSON: writer & artist **TODD KLEIN:** letterer **DANIEL VOZZO:** colorist & separator **ALISA KWITNEY:** editor

NEIL GAIMAN: creative consultant — *THE DREAMING* created by **NEIL GAIMAN**

EXCEPT THERE'S NO PUNCTUATION LIKE IN COLLEGE. NO MIDDAY CLASS. NO NIGHT LAB CLASS, NO NEXT SEMESTER.

NO GRADUATION.

AT LEAST THE WORKERS GET TO BREAK THE DAY UP. JUST HANG IN THERE 'TIL COFFEE AT TEN. JUST DEAL WITH IT UNTIL LUNCH TIME. OUTTA THERE AT FIVE.

I CAN DRINK COFFEE AND EAT DOUGHNUTS ALL DAY AND IT JUST MAKES ME FEEL LIKE A SLUG.

I LOOK AT MY SKIN AND IT'S OFF COLOR AND GREASY-LOOKING, THE WAY FLESH LOOKS IN FILMS MADE IN THE EARLY SEVENTIES.

IT'S THE OFFICE AIR. IT'S IN MY FLESH. I FEEL YELLOW INSIDE.

THE BUILDING IS JUST **WRONG**. THERE'S NO POSSIBLE WAY IT COULD BRING ENOUGH REAL OXYGEN IN.

AND THE LIGHTS. THEY COLOR EVERYTHING THE SAME. HAVE YOU EVER NOTICED THERE ARE NO SHADOWS IN AN OFFICE BUILDING?

THESE THINGS START TO SCARE ME, AND SOMETIMES I JUST NEED TO SEE THE WORLD.

NOW AND THEN, WHEN I HAVEN'T HAD ENOUGH SLEEP, I FORGET THAT THE WINDOW WON'T OPEN. I GET VERY UPSET AND HOPE THAT NO ONE CALLS OR ENTERS THE ROOM.

I TRY TO RELAX AND KEEP ALL THE DAMNED STIMULANTS FROM MAKING MY HEART RATE SOAR. I BREATHE DEEPLY AND LET THE EXHALES FLUTTER, LIKE A CHILD WHO'S FINISHED A GOOD CRY.

BUT I'M NOT GOING TO LET THE **STIMULANTS** GET TO ME. NOT LIKE MY PARTNER, WAYNE MATSOM.

IF YOU TAKE THE EASY WAY OUT, YOU JUST DON'T KNOW WHERE YOU'RE GOING TO WIND UP, DO YOU?

FOR HIM, THE OFFICE LOST AND THE BED WON. HE LIES IN A PLUSH "RECOVERY PROGRAM" SUITE ON THE COMPANY TAB WHILE I KEEP THIS BEAST TICKING.

· 226 ·
MATSOM & BIGELOW

TURF KING

THAT'S LIKE SUICIDE. THAT'S NOT FAIR.

I MAY NOT BELIEVE IN MUCH, BUT IF THERE'S A HELL WORSE THAN THIS ONE, I'M STAYING OUT AT ALL COSTS.

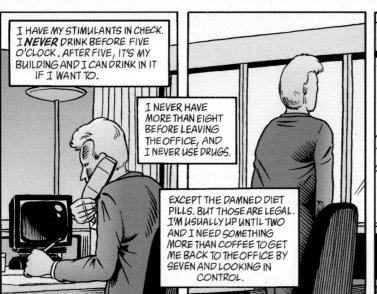

I HAVE MY STIMULANTS IN CHECK. I *NEVER* DRINK BEFORE FIVE O'CLOCK. AFTER FIVE, IT'S MY BUILDING AND I CAN DRINK IN IT IF I WANT TO.

I NEVER HAVE MORE THAN EIGHT BEFORE LEAVING THE OFFICE, AND I NEVER USE DRUGS.

EXCEPT THE DAMNED DIET PILLS. BUT THOSE ARE LEGAL. I'M USUALLY UP UNTIL TWO AND I NEED SOMETHING MORE THAN COFFEE TO GET ME BACK TO THE OFFICE BY SEVEN AND LOOKING IN CONTROL.

AND I HAVEN'T HAD A CIGARETTE IN TWELVE DAYS. NOT BAD FOR SOMEONE WHO'S TAKEN ON HIS PARTNER'S SHARE OF THE WORK.

I FIND IT AMAZING THAT IN TWO HOURS A GROUP OF MEN CAN WHIP THE WHOLE OF OUR GROUNDS INTO SHAPE AND MOVE ON.

TURF KING

INSIDE OF TWO HOURS WHAT DO I DO? MOVE PAPER. SURF CYBERSPACE. TRANSFER PROBLEMS. DOCUMENT MISERY.

I NEED SLEEP. I HAVE NO MEMORY OF SLEEP.

I HEAR THAT IF YOU DRINK BEYOND A CERTAIN AMOUNT EVERY NIGHT YOU NEVER DREAM.

TIRED. TIRED OF COFFEE.

YELLOW INSIDE.

I STARTED TO SEE THINGS. VISIONS, I GUESS. AT FIRST THEY WERE FRIGHTENING, BUT NOT LIKE THE WAY THE OFFICE FRIGHTENS ME.

LET'S SAY I WERE TO COMPARE THE VISIONS TO AN ANIMAL. A LION. ITS BEAUTY ATTRACTS ME, WHILE THE REALITY OF ITS FEROCIOUSNESS PUTS ME INTO A PANIC.

YET I'VE SEEN PICTURES OF LIONS IN CAGES, COMMANDED BY SILLY MEN IN TOP HATS. RAW POWER WITH THE LURE OF THE ABILITY TO CONTROL. THAT KIND OF FEAR.

WHAT METAPHOR DO I GIVE MY FEAR OF THE OFFICE? IT DOESN'T QUALIFY AS AN ANIMAL, IT'S AN ELEMENT. A STRIP OF PLUTONIUM HIDDEN IN MY DESK, TURNING MY BODY INTO TIRED, BLACK CANCER CELLS. NO CONTROL. JUST FEAR.

THE VISIONS ARE PRIVATE. THEY VANISH WHENEVER SOMEONE ENTERS THE ROOM.

SOMEONE LIKE CHUCK, SENIOR SALES MANAGER. I TRY TO STRIKE UP A CONVERSATION ABOUT THE GARDENERS. HE DRONES ON ABOUT THEIR SLAVE-LIKE STATION IN LIFE AND LACK OF AMBITION.

HE THEN OFFERS AS CONTRAST HIS LATEST CONQUESTS IN SALES, HIS DOLLARS, AND HIS CLIMBING OF SOCIAL STRATA.

I WOULD RATHER WORK WITH THOSE LABORERS, AND PERHAPS TASTE THEIR LION-FORCE, THAN CONSPIRE WITH THIS MAN AND HIS POCKET FULL OF PLUTONIUM. BUT THIS IS THE WORLD I HAVE BUILT, AND THESE ARE THE TYPE OF PEOPLE I MUST HIRE TO RUN IT.

PERHAPS I SHOULD SIMPLY OPEN THE DOORS AND LET THEM FREE. RENOUNCE MY LITTLE EMPIRE AS HEATHEN AND FORCE THEM OUT ON TO THE GRASS. MAKE THEM BUILD SOMETHING REAL.

BUT THEY WOULDN'T DO IT. THEY WOULD JUST SHAMBLE ALONG TO ANOTHER OFFICE, AND EMBRACE ITS BUZZING LIGHTS AND LACK OF SHADOWS.

I FIND THAT MY DAILY THOUGHTS KEEP DRIFTING TO THE WORKERS. NOT *MY* EMPLOYEES, BUT THE *REAL* WORKERS.

THEIR ACCOMPLISHMENTS CAN ACTUALLY BE VIEWED, AND I LIKE TO WATCH THEM IN ACTION WHENEVER POSSIBLE.

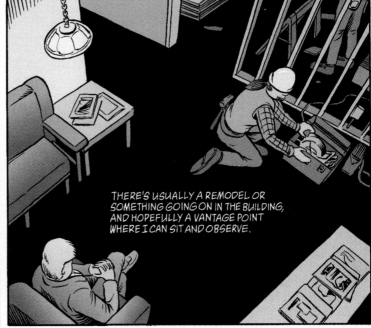

THERE'S USUALLY A REMODEL OR SOMETHING GOING ON IN THE BUILDING, AND HOPEFULLY A VANTAGE POINT WHERE I CAN SIT AND OBSERVE.

IT'S INTERESTING. I WISH THERE WAS SOME WAY I COULD JOIN THEIR TRIBE. THEY SEEM TO HAVE NO FEAR OF THE BUILDING.

THEY WORK IT. THEY MASTER IT. PERHAPS TO THEM THE BUILDING IS THE LION, AND WE, THE WHITE-COLLAR BREED, ARE THE CANCER.

JUST IMAGINE WHAT THEY WOULD BUILD WITHOUT OUR MUNDANE DIRECTIONS.

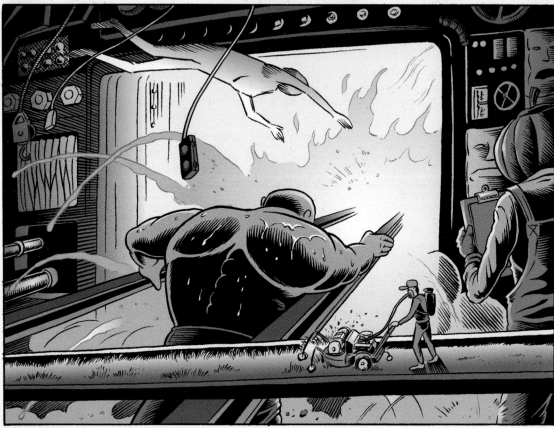

I'M SURE THEY ARE CALLING ME WITH THESE VISIONS, BUT SOMEONE ALWAYS INTERRUPTS THEM.

THIS TIME IT'S SHEILA. SHE POLITELY ASKS IF I WOULD LIKE TO ACCOMPANY HER TO THE LOUNGE FOR LUNCH.

I POLITELY DECLINE. SHE DOESN'T REALIZE I CAN'T SOCIALIZE WITH THE STAFF. IT'S BAD BUSINESS. BAD FORM.

MY ATTEMPTS AT SOCIALIZING ARE MADE AT THE WORK-RELATED MIXERS, OR IN THE WHITE-COLLAR CLUBS.

I TRY TO MAKE CONVERSATION ABOUT MY FIRST JOB, LANDSCAPING. PUTTING IN RAILROAD TIES UP IN THE CANYON WITH A PICK AND SHOVEL.

THERE WAS THIS DOG THAT WOULD TRY TO EAT MY LUNCH EVERY DAY IF I DIDN'T STICK IT UP ON A FENCE POST. I WAS YOUNG AND FIT AND HANDSOME.

WHEN I THINK OF THAT JOB, IT SEEMS MORE VIVID THAN THE LAST FIVE YEARS OF MY LIFE.

THEN I REALIZE I'VE NEVER HAD A LANDSCAPING JOB. I DON'T UNDERSTAND.

SOMETIMES I LIKE TO DRIVE AROUND THE LOWER INCOME NEIGHBORHOODS AT NIGHT. I GET TO OBSERVE THE TRIBE AS THEY PLAY.

THE BUCKHORN IS MY FAVORITE. SOMEHOW THAT DANGEROUS EXCITEMENT OF THE VISIONS APPLIES TO THE WATERING HOLE, TOO. IT DOESN'T LOOK SAFE, BUT I KNOW I COULD TAME IT. I COULD BECOME ITS FRIEND.

The BUCKHORN

LIQUOR

BUT IF I WERE TO ENTER THEIR WORLD THEY WOULD SPOT ME AS A BUILDER OF THE **WRONG** THING. A BUILDER OF A PAPER EMPIRE. NO RAILROAD TIES. NOTHING EARTHY.

IT'S TOO LATE TO CHANGE.

TOO LATE. TOO TIRED.

UNTIL THE VISIONS BECAME A VISITATION,

OH MY GOD.

YOU CAN'T SPEND FOREVER ON THAT TRIM, PAL, WE GOT LOADS O' JOBS TO GET TO YET.

IT'S JUST GONNA BE GO-GO-GO, ALL DAY LONG.

BUT WHEN THAT WHISTLE BLOWS, FIRST ROUND'S ON ME.

I....

C'MON, MAC. THE BOSS LIKES YOUR WORK, BUT YA GOTTA BE STEADY. KEEP THE PACE.

ABUDAH! TAKE HALF THE CREW TO THE OUTER REALMS AND MAKE SURE ALL THE CULVERTS ARE SOUND. I'M GONNA DROP THE NEW GUY OFF AT THE PASTURE.

YOU'RE NEW, EH? I'M ED, BY THE WAY.

MY NAME'S ROBERT.

BOB. ONE SYLLABLE DOES THE TRICK HERE.

WHERE THE HELL IS "HERE"?

IT AIN'T HELL, I SEE TO THAT, MY FRIEND. KNOW WHAT I MEAN?

UH...

HOP ON THE TRUCK. WE'RE SHIPPIN' OUT.

JUST BE CAREFUL HOW YOU HANDLE IT.

HEY!

SOME NERVE. TELLIN' ME HOW TO RUN MY CREW. A WORKIN' JOE COMES TO ME IN HIS DREAMS, I'LL TREAT 'EM SQUARE.

HECK, THERE COULD BE A LOT MORE WHERE HE CAME FROM. I COULD WIND UP THE MOST POPULAR FOCAL POINT OF THE DREAMING.

THIS COULD BE THE START OF SOMETHIN' BIG, HUGO! I COULD BE RUNNIN' THIS WHOLE SETUP SOON ENOUGH.

WELCOME, WELCOME, MY FRESH-FACED DISCIPLE! GLAD TO HAVE YOU WITH US.

I WANT YOU TO BRING MORE. PREACH MY GOSPEL, SO TO SPEAK.

BRING MORE WORKERS, YOU MEAN? FROM WHERE?

FROM THE REG'LER WORLD, OF COURSE.

BUT WHERE AM I NOW? I DON'T UNDERSTAND HOW I GOT HERE.

THIS PLACE CAN BE WHATEVER YOU WANT IT TO BE. MOST PEOPLE GO TO... WELL, LET'S NOT DWELL ON WHERE THE OTHER PEOPLE GO.

YOU'RE HERE WIT' US, THAT'S WHAT MATTERS. PART OF THE VAUNTED WORKING CLASS.

AND YOU'RE THE LEADER?

THAT'S RIGHT. LORD O' THIS WHOLE PLANE.

BUT, BOSS!

BUT I'M NO DICTATOR. I DON'T JUST SIT AROUND IN A CASTLE AND *BROOD*.

I DON'T INVOLVE MY SUBJECTS IN A LOTTA VAGUE, COBWEBBY DRAMAS, EITHER.

FIRE UP THE INGESTOR FOR THIS GOOD MAN, HUGO.

YOU WANT ME TO MOW LAWNS?

OF A SORTS. YOU NEED TO GET PUMPED UP.

WRUP CHOOM

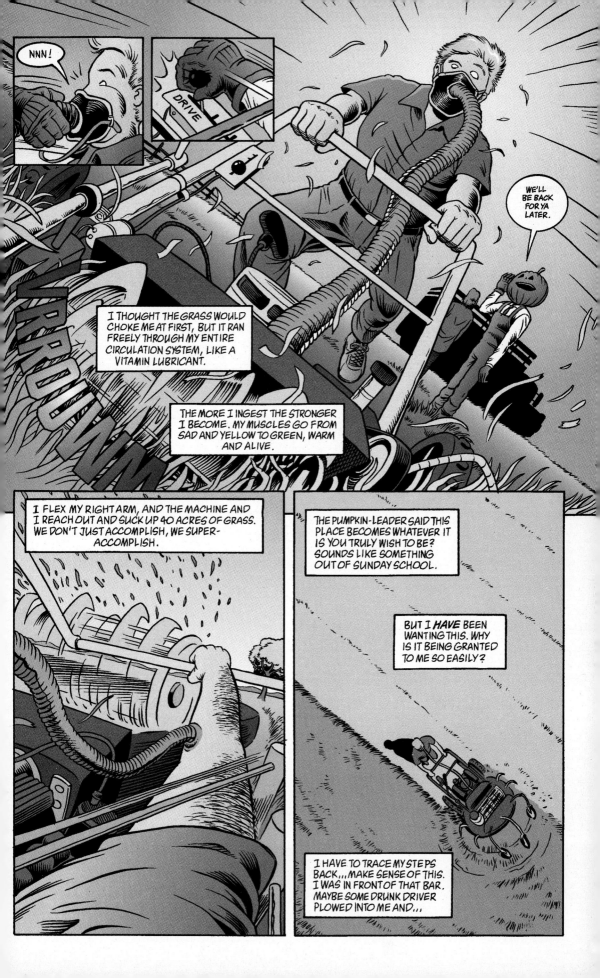

YO! BOB! TAKE A BREAK, PAL!

WHAT? I JUST STARTED!

YOU'VE BEEN CUTTIN' TURF FOR THREE HOURS. TAKE A BREAK.

OH MY GOD. I'M ALL BUFFED. I FEEL SO HEALTHY.

THE REAL YOU'S COMIN' OUT, BOB. HAVE A SMOKE.

ISN'T SMOKING A CONTRADICTION?

NOT HERE. YOU CAN SMOKE **AND** FEEL GREAT. THIS IS HEAVEN! C'MON, I'LL GIVE YA A TOUR.

HEAVEN. IT IS. IN AN OFFICE THE HOURS DRAG BY LIKE JAIL TIME. WORKING HERE, THEY WOULD RACE BY. MY THOUGHTS COULD GO WHEREVER I LET THEM.

THE WHITE COLLAR GUYS JUST DON'T GET IT. LUCIEN. CAIN AND ABEL, 'SCUSE ME FOR SAYIN' IT, BUT THEY'RE LAZY.

CAIN AND ABEL?

IT'S GOIN' AFTER THE BOSS! DISTRACT IT!

DON'T GIVE IN TO IT! SLOW IT DOWN WITH COMPLEX DREAMS!

KROWM

CHROWM

WHAT'S GOING ON? CAN'T YOU JUST SHUT IT OFF?

THAT THING'S HUNGER GETS OUTTA CONTROL SOMETIMES.

I'M KINDA CURIOUS JUST HOW MUCH IT WOULD EAT IF WE DIDN'T INTERFERE.

IT'S COMING RIGHT FOR US!

YEAH, YA CAN'T SLOW IT DOWN WITH DEBRIS. IT WANTS A WORKER.

A WORKER?!? WAITAMINUTE!!

SHUF SHUF

SORRY 'BOUT THE SCREW-UP, BOSS!

SHUF SHUF

SOMETIMES ONE OF US HAS TO MAKE A SACRIFICE IN THE LINE O' DUTY. DON'T WORRY. HUGO WILL BE BACK WITH THE NEXT BATCH O' SCENERY.

WOW.

I KNOW YA DON'T LIKE BEIN' COOPED UP INSIDE, BOB, BUT YOU'LL WANNA SEE THIS.

NO, IT'S OKAY. I LIKE CAVES AND MINE SHAFTS. THEY'RE DIFFERENT.

HOW FAR DO THEY GO?

Y'KNOW, I'M NOT REALLY SURE. A REAL THOROUGH TOUR COULD TAKE A GOOD THOUSAND YEARS.

IT'S KINDA SUBJECTIVE, BUT THESE CAVERNS ARE BELOW EVERYTHING THAT'S RELATIVE TO ME. TO MY WORK. YOU FOLLOW?

I THINK SO.

I THINK SO TOO, BOB.

I THINK YOU'RE THE FIRST ONE THAT'S REALLY RECOGNIZED ME AS THE GUY THAT RUNS THINGS HERE.

GOOD SOLID WORK COMES FROM DEEP DOWN INSIDE YA, AND IN MY REALM IT COMES OUTTA THE GROUND AS WELL.

JUST DON'T CONFUSE THIS WITH HELL.

NO, SIR.

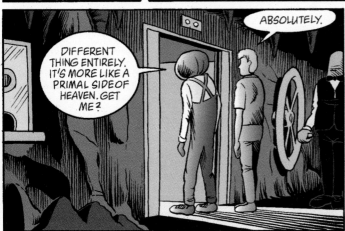

DIFFERENT THING ENTIRELY. IT'S MORE LIKE A PRIMAL SIDE OF HEAVEN. GET ME?

ABSOLUTELY.

AW, I'M GETTIN' ALL FLOWERY, JUST LIKE THE SAND-- HECK, LEMME JUST SHOW YA.

I TOLD YA. FIRST ROUND'S ON ME!

I PUNCH THE CLOCK AND THAT'S IT? I DON'T HAVE TO TAKE ANYTHING HOME WITH ME?

YOU CAN TRY AND TAKE HOME ONE OF THE GOILS FROM THE BRICKLAYIN' YARD. HAW HAW!

I'VE WORKED SO HARD, YET I FEEL MORE AWAKE.

THE NIGHT IS YOUNG. POKER STARTS AT EIGHT, MY PLACE.

WHADDYA THINK OF MY SETUP, BOB? COULD YA FIND A MORE DOWN-TO-EARTH PLACE, EVEN ON EARTH?

I DON'T THINK SO. I DON'T THINK THEY WOULD HAVE ACCEPTED ME IF I TRIED THIS KIND OF LIFE BACK HOME.

BUT IT DOESN'T MATTER NOW. HAH. I JUST WISH I COULD TELL THEM THERE WAS A BAR IN NIRVANA.

WELL, I WAS KINDA HOPIN' YOU'D TELL 'EM WHEN YOU GOT BACK.

GOT BACK? THERE ISN'T SUPPOSED TO BE ANY "GOING BACK."

YOU'LL BE HEADING BACK ANY TIME NOW. THIS WAS JUST YOUR FIRST TRIP. AN EXPLORATION TO DETERMINE WHAT YOUR, WHADDYACALL, PROCLIVITIES ARE.

WHAT?

YOU'LL BRING BACK LOTS OF WORKERS TO MY KINGDOM, RIGHT?

BUT I WANT TO STAY, PERMANENTLY.

YOU HAVE TO GO BACK TO TERRA FIRMA, PAL.

'LESS O'COURSE YA DIE.

WELL, YEAH. AND ONLY DEATH BY NATURAL CAUSES.

NO, IT DON'T MATTER HOW YOU DIE. JUST SO LONG AS YOU'RE DREAMING ABOUT *ME* WHEN YOU BITE THE BIG ONE.

I'LL SAVE A PLACE FOR YA.

UHN....

HE KNEW....HE KNEW WHAT I WANTED AND SHOWED IT TO ME IN THE FLESH.

BUT WHY? THERE'S A LOGIC TO THIS, I KNOW IT. THIS ISN'T LIKE ANY FALSE OR CONTRADICTORY RELIGION I'VE BEEN TAUGHT AS A CHILD.

IT'S ALL BACKWARDS. THEY'LL KEEP TELLING US TO WAIT. TO WAIT AND WAIT THROUGH A LIFE OF HELL TO GET TO HEAVEN.

BUT THEY'VE BEEN SO INCREDIBLY WRONG ON THE REQUIREMENTS TO GET TO HEAVEN.

HOW GOD IS NOT A BEARDED MAN, BUT A FACE CARVED IN A GOURD. DID THE PAGANS HAVE IT RIGHT?

YOU DON'T LEARN OF HEAVEN FROM A BOOK, THEN PATIENTLY WAIT TO REACH IT. WHY WOULD THAT PLEASE HIM?

HE PATIENTLY WAITS FOR YOU TO DISCOVER THAT HEAVEN, THEN CALLS YOU TO IT.

SO LONG AS YOU DREAM OF *HIM*, AS YOU ENTER YOUR FINAL NIGHT'S REST...

WELL, HUGO. ANOTHER DAY'S WORK. STILL NO SIGN OF THAT DREAMER WE HAD ON THE CREW.

HEY! WHO'S THE *NEW* DUDE?

THAT'S BOB. DON'T TALK TOO FAST, HE'S HANDICAPPED.

NAW, BOSS. IT'S BEEN WEEKS. HE DIDN'T START NO TREND AFTER ALL.

HUGO

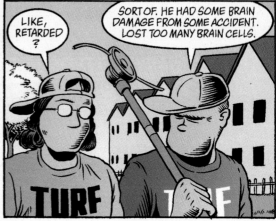

LIKE, RETARDED?

SORT OF. HE HAD SOME BRAIN DAMAGE FROM SOME ACCIDENT. LOST TOO MANY BRAIN CELLS.

TURF

NOPE. I SHOULDA KNOWN. A WORKIN' GUY LIKE ME DON'T BECOME KING. BUT I HELPED OUT OL' BOB, THOUGH. THAT'S GOOD FOR SOMETHIN'.

BUT HE'S GREAT WITH A THIRTY-SIX. RIGHT, BOB?

TURF KING

saying grace now, pleeze.

BOB DIDN'T COME BACK BECAUSE, IPSO FACTO, HE'S CONTENT IN THE REAL WORLD. I'LL TAKE CREDIT FOR THAT.

thank you, to the pumpkin man....

END

The DREAMING

"Ice"

PETER HOGAN
····WRITER····

GARY AMARO
····ARTIST····

DANIEL VOZZO
COLORS & SEPS.

ALISA KWITNEY
····EDITOR····

TODD KLEIN
····LETTERS····

NEIL GAIMAN
····CONSULTANT····

THE DREAMING
CREATED BY
NEIL GAIMAN

YES, OF COURSE I KNOW WHAT BLOODY *DAY* IT IS...

LOOK, I DON'T *CARE.* JUST PAY WHAT-EVER IT TAKES TO MAKE THINGS *HAPPEN,* OKAY?

NOW, THEY'LL BE CROSSING THE RIVER AT *WATERLOO,* SO YOU'LL NEED TO BLOCK SIDESTREETS FOR A MILE OR SO, NORTH *AND* SOUTH... I KNOW TRAFFIC SHOULD BE ALMOST NON-EXISTENT AT MIDNIGHT, BUT LET'S BE *THOROUGH* HERE.

GOOD. AND I WANT UPDATES *HALF-HOURLY* FROM NOW ON, UNDER-STOOD?

COFFEE...

THANKS--AND KEEP IT COMING--IT'S GOING TO BE A *LONG* DAY...

PROBLEMS?

LONDON, IN *WINTER.*

THAT ABOUT SUMS IT UP.

WHY DOES WINTER ALWAYS *SURPRISE* THE ENGLISH? ONE SNOWFLAKE AND THE WHOLE *CITY* GRINDS TO A HALT...

JUST *ONCE,* I WISH HE'D PICK SOMEWHERE *CIVILIZED* TO RACE.

LAST YEAR YOU WERE COMPLAINING BECAUSE IT WAS *SHANGHAI.* AT LEAST YOU WON'T HAVE TO WORRY ABOUT *RICKSHAWS* THIS TIME...

DON'T *REMIND* ME.

THE SOONER THIS IS *OVER,* THE HAPPIER I'LL BE...

THE DREAMING.

WUH *WELL?*

WELL *WHAT?*

WHAT DID HE SUH *SAY?*

HE SAID HE HAS NO OB-JECTIONS...

OH. SO DOES THAT MUH MEAN YOU'LL BE LUH LUH *LEAVING* SOON?

NO TIME LIKE THE PRESENT.

NUH *NOW?* BUT... WHO'S GOING TO MUH MIND THE LUH *LIBRARY?*

BECAUSE *I'M* NOT LOOKING AFTER IT AGAIN. THE BOOKS ALWAYS SNUH *SNIGGER* BEHIND MY BUH *BACK*...

AND IT'S NUH *NOT* VERY *NICE.*

THANK YOU FOR YOUR CONCERN, ABEL. BUT I HAVE ALREADY *APPOINTED* A TEMPORARY CARETAKER, SO EVERYTHING WILL BE JUST *FINE*...

YO! LOOSHY!

SO, ARE WE IN BUSINESS, OR WHAT?

I HOPE.

YOU CAN'T BE SUH SERIOUS?

YOU'RE GOING TO LET HUH HIM GUARD ALL THE GRUH GRUH GRIMOIRES AND BOOKS OF PUH POWER? YOU'D RATHER HAVE HUH HIM THAN MUH ME?

MERVYN HAS BEEN FULLY BRIEFED ON EMERGENCY PROCEDURES, AND HE HAS MY UTMOST CONFIDENCE...

FAILING WHICH, HE ALSO HAS A NOTE OF MY MOBILE PHONE NUMBER.

NOW, IF YOU'LL EXCUSE ME, I MUST GET READY.

I HOPE THIS AIN'T GONNA TAKE LONG, LOOSH. I MEAN, NO OFFENSE, BUT I GOTTA TON A' REAL WORK TO DO.

NUTS 'N' BOLTS STUFF, Y' KNOW?

I'LL BE AS QUICK AS I CAN...

ARE THESE REALLY THE WARMEST COATS WE'VE GOT?

YUP. YOU WANT I SHOULD GO HUNT DOWN SOMETHING WITH FUR ON IT? A BEAR, MAYBE?

NO, THANK YOU. I'M SURE THIS WILL SUFFICE.

YOU'RE HEADED SOMEWHERE COLD, RIGHT? ME, I'M STRICTLY A CLUB MED KINDA GUY...

GOODBYE, MERVYN...I'LL CALL IF I'M DELAYED.

33

SOUTH LONDON : AT MIDDLE-NIGHT, A BLACK McLAREN F1 MATERIALIZES AT CRYSTAL PALACE, ON A ROAD THAT IS MORE ICE THAN ASPHALT....

THE CAR IS *ALREADY* TRAVELLING AT FIFTY M.P.H., ITS TIRES FINDING TRACTION WHERE NONE EXISTS.

LESS THAN FIVE SECONDS ELAPSE BEFORE THE SECOND CAR (IDENTICAL, BUT WHITE) APPEARS, A PALE SHADOW TRAILING IN THE WAKE OF ITS TWIN....

INSIDE *BOTH* CARS SITS THE BEING THE ROMANS NAMED JANUS. AT THE GATE OF THE YEAR, THE GOD OF DOORWAYS IS CHASING HIS TAIL.

THIS RACE CARVES A JAGGED PATH THROUGH THE ANCIENT CAPITAL, CLIPPING ITS CENTER BEFORE BOUNDING NORTHWARDS AGAIN. IMPROBABLY, *EVERY* TRAFFIC LIGHT UPON THE ROUTE REMAINS AT GREEN UNTIL BOTH CARS HAVE PASSED.

THE COMPUTER OPERATOR RESPONSIBLE FOR ARRANGING THIS (RECRUITED BY CANASTA) WILL TOMORROW QUIT HIS JOB AND DEPART FOR THE CARIBBEAN WITH AN ATTACHÉ CASE OF BEARER BONDS.

AT 12:37 AM BOTH VEHICLES ABRUPTLY *LEAVE* OUR PLANE OF EXISTENCE JUST NORTH OF COLINDALE. SEVERAL POLICE OFFICERS WHO WITNESS THE EVENT WILL LATER RECEIVE EXTENSIVE COUNSELING.

THERE HAVE BEEN THE USUAL NUMBER OF MINOR TRAFFIC ACCIDENTS THIS YEAR, BUT--MIRACULOUSLY--ONLY *ONE* PEDESTRIAN FATALITY.

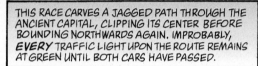

THE GOD OF TRANSPORT IS CONTENT.

THE RACE RUN, HE CAN NOW TURN HIS ATTENTION TO THE PROBLEMS OF **WARMER** CLIMES, WHICH HE HAS NEGLECTED OF LATE.

NEW YORK CITY, NEW YEAR'S DAY.

The Green Dragon

'APPY **NOO** YEAR!

THIS HEMISPHERE WILL BE COMPARATIVELY QUIET FOR SEVERAL DAYS TO COME: IT IS A TIME OF **ICE**, AND LITTLE WILL BE MOVING.

HELLO, BRAD. YOU MADE IT, THEN?

HI, NUALA. YEAH, IT'S REALLY SOMETHIN', ISN'T IT?

PROBABLY LOADS OF PEOPLE'RE STILL TRYING TO GET HOME AFTER THE HOLIDAYS--HALF THE DAMN **COUNTRY'S** SNOWBOUND.

TAPE'S FINISHED-- SHALL I STICK SOMETHING ELSE ON?

THINGS'RE PRETTY QUIET, HUH?

YES. I SUPPOSE THE WEATHER'S KEEPING EVERYBODY IN.

KEEP IT GENTLE, THEN. MOST OF THESE ARE NURSING LAST NIGHT'S SORE HEADS.

SOMETHING CLASSICAL, MAYBE.

GENTLE IT IS...

CLIK

MMMMMMMM UM MMMM.

CHICKEN.

THEN I'LL ASK HER.

HEY, NOOLA--CAN WE GET A COUPLE MORE BEERS OVER HERE?

SURELY...

AND THE NAME'S NU-AH-LA.

SO...NU-AH-LA... YOU LIKE MUSIC, HUH?

I LIKE IT WELL ENOUGH...

BILLY HERE'S A SONGWRITER. BEEN TO NASHVILLE AN' EVERYTHIN'...

HI...

PLEASED TO MEET YOU, BILLY.

LIKEWISE. ER, CAN I BUY YOU A DRINK?

THE BORDER WORLDS, BETWEEN FAERIE AND LLINOR...

WHERE'S MY *DRINK?*

I CLOSED MY EYES FOR BUT THE *BRIEFEST* OF MOMENTS, ONLY TO FIND THAT SOME THIEVING FOOTPAD HAS *STOLEN* IT. WHAT MANNER OF ESTABLISHMENT *IS* THIS?

I HAD A *BOTTLE* HERE JUST NOW.

I MOVED IT, FOR SAFETY'S SAKE, WHEN YOU FELL OFF YOUR CHAIR. YOU'VE BEEN SLEEPING IT OFF ALL DAY...

...AND I *AM* THE MANAGEMENT.

I SHALL COMPLAIN TO THE *MANAGEMENT,* BE *SURE* THAT I WILL...

HERE'S YOUR BOTTLE.

SO, WILL YOU BE SETTLING YOUR *BILL* NOW?

LATER. AND BRING ME *ANOTHER* BOTTLE...

SOMEHOW I KNEW YOU WERE GOING TO SAY...

WELL, IF MY DOOM HAS COME UPON ME, IT SHALL AT LEAST BE A TALE WORTH THE TELLING. *INNKEEPER,* FETCH PARCHMENT, AND I SHALL *DICTATE:*

" THE BALLAD OF *BRAVE* CLURACAN, AND HOW HIS DEATH CAME *DEAR* IN THE BUYING."

SHING

I CONFESS I AM *SURPRISED,* BROTHER, TO FIND YOU THIS *SOBER...*

THOUGHT ME AN EASY MARK, DID YE? WELL, DANGER'S THE VERY THING FOR CLEARING THE HEAD, I FIND...

SHALL WE BE *ABOUT* IT?

WHOA!

IF YOU TWO ARE GOING TO KILL EACH OTHER, CAN WE AT LEAST *SHUT* THE BLOODY *DOOR* BEFORE YOU START...

RIGHT-- SURVIVOR PAYS FOR DAMAGES, UNDERSTOOD? AND I *DON'T* WANT MY OTHER CUSTOMERS INJURED.

OTHERWISE, START AT YOUR WILL.

WHAT OTHER CUSTOMERS?

40

OLD WILF, SAT OVER IN THE CORNER, THERE.

EVENIN'.

DON'T MIND ME, LADS--YOU JUST CARRY ON.

I SAID *PEACE*, INNKEEPER, DID I NOT? AND I MEANT IT TRULY...

PUT UP YOUR SWORD, BROTHER. I WOULD DRINK WINE WITH YOU, IF YOU BE WILLING.

DRINK OR FIGHT, IT'S ALL ONE TO ME.

BUT YOU CAN BUY YOUR *OWN* DAMN WINE. *THAT* BOTTLE'S *MINE*.

WELL, *SIT*, THEN... THAT'S WHAT CHAIRS ARE FOR.

ANOTHER BOTTLE, INN-KEEPER.

NEW YORK:

'SCUSE ME, FOLKS--GOTTA DO THE *DO*.

SO... WHERE WERE WE?

YOU WERE SAYIN' YOU DIDN'T LIKE LOVE SONGS.

NO, IT'S NOT THAT. IT'S JUST THAT I THINK THEY'RE, WELL... *DISHONEST,* I SUPPOSE.

SEE, THE HAPPY ONES AREN'T ABOUT LOVE. THEY'RE ABOUT BEING *MAD* WITH LOVE, AND IN LOVE WITH THAT FEELING...

AND THEY'RE FINE, GIDDY THINGS, BUT THEY AREN'T *TRUE.*

AND THE *SAD* ONES... WELL, THEY'RE NOT ABOUT LOVE *EITHER.*

THEY'RE ABOUT *PAIN,* AND HURT, AND PEOPLE ONLY LIKE THEM WHEN THAT'S HOW THEY'RE FEELING. THE SONGS SAY, "*I'VE* HAD IT BAD, TOO--MAYBE WORSE THAN YOU. I KNOW WHAT IT'S *LIKE.*"

AND THAT'S ALL THEY ARE: JUST FRIENDLY VOICES TO COMFORT YOU IN THE DARK.

I STILL QUITE *LIKE* THEM, MIND.

YEAH? UH, *SPEAKIN'* OF FRIENDLY VOICES... I WAS WONDERIN' IF MAYBE YOU'D CARE TO... *GO* SOMEWHERE LATER, AND *TALK*...

MAYBE I COULD EVEN PLAY YOU SOME OF MY SONGS...

I ...*THANK* YOU, BILLY, FOR THE COMPLIMENT YOU PAY ME, BUT... I THINK NOT.

SEE, I'M NOT REALLY IN THE MARKET FOR ...SONGS.

SO PERHAPS YOU SHOULD SEEK ANOTHER AUDIEN...

LUCIEN...

OH, IT'S SO GOOD TO SEE YOU.

A LITTLE ON THE COLD SIDE, AT THE MOMENT...

ARE YOU HERE TO SEE ME? I SUPPOSE YOU MUST BE, ARE YOU STAYING LONG? COME AND SIT DOWN, HOW ARE YOU?

WHAT'S HE GOT THAT I DON'T?

PROB'LY JUST A RELATIVE, DON'T SWEAT IT. I THINK YOU STILL GOT A CHANCE HERE...

MY SHIFT ENDS IN HALF AN HOUR, AND THEN I'M GOING TO BUY YOU DINNER...

BUT FIRST YOU NEED A DRINK, TO WARM YOU. SO, WHAT SHALL IT BE?

OH, DEAR. I'M A LITTLE OUT OF PRACTICE AT THIS...

PERHAPS...A SMALL GLASS OF PORT? OR ELSE... WHAT'S THAT DRINK YOUR BROTHER LIKES?

NOW THAT I COULDN'T SAY...

...FOR MY BROTHER WILL DRINK ANYTHING, I FEAR.

HERE'S MUD ON YER ANTLERS...

AND A HEALTH UNTO YOU.

I *HAD* THOUGHT TO FIND YOU ON THE ROAD, THE CLURACAN. SHOULD YOU NOT BE ABROAD ON YOUR QUEEN'S BUSINESS?

WHAT, AND BE HUNTED DOWN LIKE A DOG, TO DIE ALONE ON THE CRUEL COLD ICE? NO *THANK* YE!

I'LL MAKE MY STAND *HERE*, WHERE THE HEARTH AND THE WINE ARE WARM.

DO YOUR ⌐HIC⌐ *WORST.*

AND HAVE I NOT SAID THAT I MEAN YOU NO HARM?

FOR WHERE'S THE SENSE OR GLORY IN KILLING *HALF* A MAN? SURE, I'D RATHER SEE YOU *WHOLE* FIRST.

OR WILL YOU BE SPENDING *ALL* YOUR DAYS HIDING BEHIND GLASS?

ASH AND *IRON!* I'LL *NOT* BE LECTURED TO BY, BY,... TALKING *VENISON.*

AND MY,... *LIFE* IS *NO* AFFAIR OF YOURS.

AH, BUT IT *IS*, BROTHER. FOR IF THE END OF YOU IS WHAT I'M *FOR*, THEN WHERE WILL *I* BE WHEN YOU ARE DEAD AND GONE?

OH, DESTROY YOU I *MUST*, IN TIME, FOR THAT IS MY *LOT*-- BUT WE'VE MANY A LONG EVENING TO PASS UNTIL THEN. UNLESS THE BOTTLE KILLS YE *FIRST*, OF COURSE,...

I'M THINKING I'M IN NO HASTE TO BE FINDING OUT.

AH, FALL IN A *BOG*, WHY DON'T YE?

IT SEEMS BY SOME ... TRIFLING DEED OR WORD I HAVE *OFFENDED* THE QUEEN'S MAJESTY.

AND SO, AS A JEST AND A PUNISHMENT, I HAVE BEEN APPOINTED ENVOY TO THE COURT OF *LLINOR* ... WHERE IT IS THE CUSTOM FOR VISITING AMBASSADORS TO *WED* WITH A LADY OF THE ROYAL HOUSE.

FOR THOUGH SHE WELL KNOWS THIS CUSTOM IS NEITHER TO MY TASTE NOR MY NATURE, IT ... *AMUSES* TITANIA TO PICTURE ME THUS, *RUTTING* AT HER BIDDING.

BUT IF I DO *NOT* COMPLY, 'TIS BANISHMENT FOR CERTAIN. AND SO ... I *SIT* HERE, AND *PROCRASTINATE* ...

BROTHER, *I* DO NOT *SHARE* YOUR NATURE.

AH, WELL. IT TAKES ALL SORTS, SO THEY SAY, AND I'M A BROADMINDED SOUL.

'TIS A WASTE OF A HANDSOME FACE, MIND, ...

D'YE NOT GRASP MY *MEANING*, THE CLURACAN?

SO ... YOU PREFER *WOMEN*, THEN?

I DO.

I COULD *BE* YOU, AND PLAY YOUR ROLE IN THIS.

BETTER YOU SHOULD BEAR TITANIA'S AMUSEMENT THAN HER ANGER, IS IT NOT SO?

YOU'D *DO* THIS FOR ME?

'TIS HARDLY A *HARDSHIP*.

UNLESS THE MAID BE *UGLY*, ...

SO, HOW'D YOU LIKE THE LOOK OF ME NOW?

I'M USING A *LITTLE* MORE GLAMOUR THAN USUAL, JUST TO HIDE MY EARS AND PASS FOR HUMAN.... BUT OTHERWISE, THIS IS HOW I AM.

IT'S VERY, UM, BECOMING.

WELL, *I* LIKE IT. AND THAT'S HOW I FEEL...

AS IF I'M *BECOMING* SOMETHING.... *ME*, I SUPPOSE. PERHAPS FOR THE FIRST TIME.

AND IT'S EXCITING. I MEAN, I DON'T KNOW *WHERE* I'M JOURNEYING, BUT IT *FEELS* LIKE THE RIGHT DIRECTION.

I MUST SAY, I'M RELIEVED TO FIND YOU IN SUCH GOOD SPIRITS. I'LL ADMIT I WAS RATHER... *CONCERNED* ABOUT YOU.

I MEAN, WE *ALL* WERE.

MY EMPLOYER HAS NO OBJECTIONS, AND I'M SURE MERVYN COULD LOCATE THE CURRENT WHEREABOUTS OF YOUR OLD LIVING QUARTERS...

OH...

OR WE COULD HAVE *NEW* ONES BUILT, IF YOU'D *PREFER*...

NO...

THANK YOU, LUCIEN, BUT... THAT'S THE *PAST* NOW. I COULDN'T RETURN THERE...

AT LEAST, NOT YET. *SOMEDAY* I'LL COME FOR A VISIT, I PROMISE...

AND HOW WAS YOUR MEAL? EVERYTHING ALL RIGHT?

THANK YOU, MARIO, IT WAS DELICIOUS...

COULD WE GET THE CHECK NOW, PLEASE?

COMING RIGHT AWAY.

BUT HERE NOW-- WE'VE SPENT ALL EVENING TALKING ABOUT ME. HOW ARE THINGS WITH *YOU* THESE DAYS? AND WITH THE OTHERS?

OH, YOU KNOW...THIS AND THAT...

THE USUAL.

THANK YOU, MARIO.

SO, er, WILL YOU BE *STAYING* ON EARTH?

FOR A WHILE, I THINK.

THERE'S SO MUCH *LIFE* HERE, SO MUCH TO *SEE*...

OH, LOOK-- IT SEEMS TO HAVE STOPPED SNOWING.

MAYBE WE'RE OVER THE WORST OF IT NOW...

YES... LET'S HOPE SO.

COME ON, THEN--I'LL WALK YOU HOME.

'TIS **SETTLED**, THEN.

I'D WISH YOU GOOD LUCK, BUT I'VE NO DESIRE TO BE THOUGHT CRUDE.

DO YOU BIDE HERE TILL I RETURN, THAT YOU MAY REPORT ACCURATELY TO THE QUEEN...

AND WHERE ELSE WOULD I BE?

RIGHT-- DRINKS ALL **ROUND**, I THINK.

SO, WHAT ARE WE CELE-BRATING?

I HAVE **NO** IDEA. WHAT WERE WE CELEBRATING LAST NIGHT?

THE NEW YEAR ON A PLACE CALLED EARTH, OR SO YOU CLAIMED.

THEN TONIGHT IT'LL BE...THE DAY AFTER **THAT** THAT WE'RE CELEBRATING...

OR ELSE WE MIGHT DRINK TO... MY BROTHER'S STAG NIGHT.

I CAN SCARCE BELIEVE I JUST SAID THAT.

MINE'S A PINT.

SO THE BANE OF CLURACAN CAME IN TIME TO THE COURT OF LLINOR, AND WAS WELCOMED AS BEFITS AN AMBASSADOR OF FAERIE.

IN ACCORDANCE WITH THEIR CUSTOMS, HIS WEDDING TOOK PLACE THAT VERY DAY.

AND A GLAD DAY IT WAS, FOR BRIDE AND GROOM FOUND FAVOR IN EACH OTHER'S EYES, AND THEIR DUTY DID NOT SEEM UNPLEASANT TO THEM.

IN THE HEART OF WINTER THEY FOUND FIRE, AND-- ALL UNHOPED FOR--*MORE*: A WARMTH THAT *GREW*, THROUGHOUT THE LONG NIGHTS OF THEIR TALKING.

HE TARRIED IN THAT KINGDOM A WEEK AND A DAY, AND THE TIME OF HIS LEAVING CAME *HARD* UPON HIM. BUT OTHER DUTIES HAD HE...

SO HE SWORE HIS LOVE AN OATH OF RETURN, AND THEN TURNED HIS FACE TO THE WIND, ON THE BROAD WILD ROAD THAT LEADS TO ALL WORLDS.

THOUGH HE KNEW IT NOT, BEFORE HIS OATH'S FULFILLMENT THEIR UNION WOULD BEAR FRUIT.

FOR ALL THINGS FIND THEIR SEASON...

...AND *EVERY* SEASON PASSES.

The End

"Souvenirs"

THE DREAMING. THE CITADEL OF THE CORINTHIAN.

WHEN THE NIGHTMARE CAME BACK FROM SWARTALFHEIM, CAME BACK WITH THE KID, THE HIPPOGRIFF GUARDING THE CASTLE'S GATES SAID THEY'D **MEANT** TO PREPARE APARTMENTS FOR HIM. BEFORE THINGS GOT SO OUT OF HAND...

BUT THIS PLACE HE FOUND INSTEAD, SOMETHING SHINY THAT FELL FROM THE HEAVENS (OR HELLS) EONS AGO. **PERFECT** FOR HIS PURPOSES, AND NO COURTLY DISTRACTIONS OR PRYING EYES.

SOUVENIRS
part one

Caitlin R. Kiernan, writer
Peter Doherty, artist
Todd Klein, letterer
Daniel Vozzo, colorist & seps
Jennifer Lee, assistant editor
Alisa Kwitney, editor
Neil Gaiman, consultant

THE DREAMING created by Neil Gaiman

BETTER THIS WAY. THE SOLITUDE, AND NO ONE CAN HEAR HIM WHEN HE WAKES, SWEATCOLD AND CRYING, OR SCREAMING, FROM THE ODD DREAMS THAT NIGHTMARES HAVE.

HE'D RATHER THERE WAS NO ONE ELSE AROUND TO HEAR TO ASK QUESTIONS OR OFFER WELL-MEANT AND EMPTY COMFORT.

THESE THINGS ARE *HIS*, AND HIS ALONE.

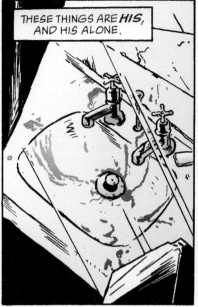

AN *APPETITE* SOMEONE ELSE MIGHT HAVE HAD, ONCE, SOMEONE HE MIGHT HAVE BEEN BEFORE.

FORGOTTEN CRAVINGS REMEMBERED IN *CRIMSON GLIMPSES.*

THE STIRRING BETWEEN HIS LEGS IS THERE NOT IN SPITE OF THE THINGS HE SEES...

...BUT *BECAUSE* OF THEM.

AND HE THINKS MAYBE HE'S BEGINNING TO UNDERSTAND THE REASON FOR THE FALL.

NEAR ATHENS, GEORGIA.

YOU'RE SURE HIS EYES WERE OPEN?

YOU'RE SURE HE DIDN'T CLOSE HIS EYES? THAT HE KNEW WHAT WAS HAP-PENING?

GABRIEL ANGEL, I SWEAR, THAT PRETTY CHILD NEVER EVEN BLINKED.

AN UTTERLY FASCINATING VOLUME, ACTUALLY. ARE YOU CERTAIN YOU'VE NEVER READ IT?

I DON'T, UH, REALLY READ THAT MUCH, YOU KNOW.

AH, THAT'S A SHAME.

YEAH. I GUESS SO. BUT YOU WERE SAYING SOMETHING ABOUT...

AH, YES, WELL, THAT PARTICULAR BOOK WAS A RECURRING DREAM THAT HUYGENS WAS HAVING TOWARD THE END OF 1657, IN WHICH HE WAS GRINDING A LENS FOR A TELESCOPE FIVE METERS LONG AND ARGUING ENDLESSLY WITH ISAAC NEWTON ABOUT SPERMATOZOA.

I DIDN'T MEAN ABOUT THE BOOK. WHAT YOU WERE SAYING BEFORE THAT, WHY YOU WANTED TO TALK TO ME.

HOLLYWOODLAND WILLIAM FAULKNER

MMM. OH, YES. *THAT.* THE MATTER OF THE CORINTHIAN.

UH, YEAH. THAT.

I'M THE ONE WHO ACTUALLY DISCOVERED THAT THE ORIGINAL INCARNATION OF THAT NIGHTMARE WAS MISSING, YOU KNOW.

THAT HE HAD LEFT THE DREAMING. SO YOU CAN UNDERSTAND MY CONCERN OVER THIS DEVELOPMENT.

YEAH. I GUESS I CAN.

WELL, AT ANY RATE, A BREACH IS A PHENOMENON SIMILAR, IN MOST RESPECTS AND IN ITS BASIC PROPERTIES, TO A WORMHOLE. DO YOU UNDERSTAND WORMHOLES?

I DON'T GUESS WE'RE TALKING ABOUT *EARTHWORMS*, ARE WE?

NO. WE *AREN'T*. NEVER MIND WORMHOLES, MATTHEW.

THERE'S A THINNING PLACE BETWEEN THE DREAMING AND THE WAKING WORLDS.

IF THAT THIN PLACE IS ALLOWED TO ACTUALLY TEAR ITSELF OPEN, IT WOULD BECOME A BREACH. YOU MIGHT THINK OF IT AS A SORT OF SHORTCUT OR TUNNEL BETWEEN WORLDS.

AND THAT WOULD BE BAD...?

DOORS LEFT OPEN ARE *NEVER* GOOD THINGS, MATTHEW. ESPECIALLY DOORS THAT NEVER SHOULD HAVE BEEN BUILT TO BEGIN WITH.

THE BREACH IS FORMING BECAUSE THE CORINTHIAN LEFT SCARS DURING HIS TIME IN THE WAKING WORLD.

A PREOCCUPATION, PERHAPS, ON THE PART OF SOMEONE THAT HE ENCOUNTERED BUT DIDN'T ACTUALLY KILL, OR A SUBCONSCIOUS OBSESSION BY THE *NEW* CORINTHIAN WITH SOME BIT OF QUASI-INHERITED MEMORY OR...

...OR COLLECTIVE *OWWW!*

BOTHER.

MATTHEW, I DON'T SUPPOSE YOU WOULD BE SO KIND AS TO FLY DOWN AND RETRIEVE MY GLASSES FOR ME?

HE GIVES ME THE CREEPING HEEBIE-JEEBIES, *THAT'S* WHY.

BE THAT AS IT MAY, MATTHEW, WE DO WHAT IS *REQUIRED* OF US.

A LOT EASIER TO JUST GO THAN MAKE A FUSS, WHEN HE KNOWS HE'D ONLY HAVE LOST ANYWAY. AND THERE'S ALWAYS THE OFF CHANCE THAT HE'LL GET LUCKY AND THE THERMALS OR DOWNDRAFTS WILL PLUCK HIM FROM THE SKY AND TOSS HIM BROKEN TO THE PLAINS BELOW.

BUT HE ISN'T FEELING VERY LUCKY TODAY, TO TELL THE GOD'S HONEST TRUTH.

SLIPPING OUT OF THE CRACKLING HAZE THAT PASSES FOR DAYLIGHT THIS FAR OUT, INTO THE POLISHED MIRROR HALLS...

...AND HE WOULD ALMOST AS SOON CLOSE HIS EYES, FLY HEADLONG INTO THE WALLS THAT WRITHE AND BOIL WITH A BILLION PERSONAL HELLS.

BUT HE SUSPECTS THIS WOULD BE AN EVEN WORSE PLACE TO BE DEAD THAN ALIVE.

IN FACT, HE'S PRETTY GODDAMN *SURE* OF IT.

HEY THERE, BIRDIE.

MHM, YEAH. HEY, IF I'M INTERRUPTING SOMETHING I COULD MAYBE COME BACK LATER.

...OR NOT.

YOU MEAN *THIS?* NO. ACTUALLY, I WAS JUST ABOUT DONE WITH THIS.

SO, WHO SENT YOU, BIRDIE? I ASSUME YOU WEREN'T JUST FEELING NEIGHBORLY.

LUCIEN SAID... WELL, I REALLY DIDN'T UNDERSTAND MOST OF IT, BUT HE THINKS YOU MIGHT BE CONSIDERING DOING WHAT THE *FIRST* CORINTHIAN DID AND, WELL, YOU KNOW, SKIPPING OUT ON US.

AND DON'T CALL ME "BIRDIE."

THE LIBRARIAN SHOULD LEARN TO KEEP HIS NOSE IN HIS BOOKS AND OUT OF PLACES WHERE IT ISN'T WELCOME.

HE WAS THE ONE WHO HAD TO TELL THE, UM, OLD BOSS WHEN YOU, I MEAN, WHEN YOUR, UH, WHEN THE *FIRST* CORINTHIAN LEFT THE DREAMING.

SO HE SENT *YOU* TO KEEP AN EYE ON ME?

WHY DON'T YOU SAVE US *BOTH* SOME TIME, CUT THE CRAP, AND JUST TELL ME WHAT'S GOING ON.

SOMEONE OUT THERE CAN'T GET ME OUT OF HIS HEAD, BIRDIE.

SOMEONE OUT THERE IS STARTING TO BELIEVE HE *IS* ME, AND IT'S BEEN KEEPING ME UP NIGHTS, IF YOU KNOW WHAT I MEAN.

SOMEONE YOU HURT BEFORE... I MEAN...

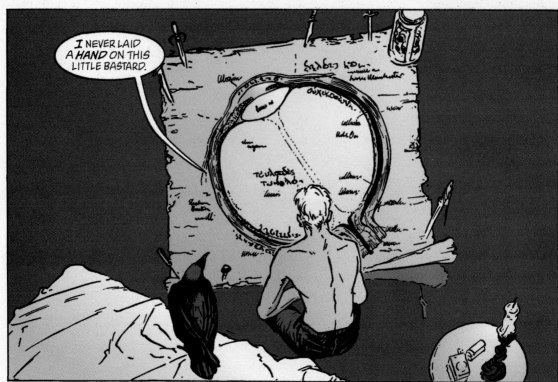

I NEVER LAID A **HAND** ON THIS LITTLE BASTARD.

I'VE BEEN RIGHT HERE, DOING MY JOB, MY PRESCRIBED **DUTY**, PLAYING LOOKING GLASS FOR EVERY CRINGING MORTAL TOO AFRAID OF WHO OR WHAT THEY REALLY ARE TO FACE IT WHILE THEY'RE AWAKE.

SINCE MY REBIRTH,...SINCE **MY BIRTH,** I'VE TAKEN THE EYES OF A FRENCH-FRIED CORPSE, A WOLF, AND A GOD. AND THAT'S ALL.

HEY! THAT'S NOT WHAT I MEANT.

I **KNOW** WHAT YOU MEANT. FOR A WHILE I THOUGHT I WAS BEGINNING TO REMEMBER THINGS,...

...BUT IT'S NOT REALLY NECESSARY TO REMEMBER. WHY BOTHER, WHEN THERE ARE SO MANY PEOPLE TO DO IT **FOR** YOU.

C'MON. LET'S GO FOR A WALK, LITTLE BIRD.

THE THRESHOLD, ATLANTA.

THEY'VE COME HERE, ALL OF THEM, TO PLAY THESE GAMES OF PAIN AND POWER.

THE SUBMISSIVES TO SPEAK WHEN THEY'RE SPOKEN TO, TO WATCH THE FLOOR AND WAIT FOR THE CUE TO FLINCH. THE DOMS AND DOMINAS TO ADMINISTER DESIRED PUNISHMENT, TO POSE AND PANTOMIME DISDAIN.

CAREFUL CHOREOGRAPHY AND ACCIDENTAL HINTS OF TRUER HUNGERS, BUT EACH PROTECTED BY SAFE-WORDS AND THE RIGID CODE OF CONDUCT OF THE SEXUAL UNDERGROUND.

DRAWING BLOOD IS GROUNDS FOR IMMEDIATE EJECTION FROM THE PREMISES.

THERE ARE NO *REAL* PREDATORS HERE.

IS THERE SOME PLACE PRIVATE WE CAN PLAY?

YES, MISTRESS. THERE ARE ROOMS IN THE BACK.

BROWN, GABRIEL. HIS EYES ARE HAZEL BROWN.

THAT THE SOUL CAN TAKE A CUT SO DEEP AND RAGGED THE BODY NEVER HEALS, NEVER FORGETS THE COLD STEEL KISS OF THE KNIFE OR RAZOR--

--THE WORDS THAT FRAMED THE WOUND, THOUGH TIME GOES ON AND THE WORLD SPINS ITS CAROUSEL OF BLISTER WHITE SUMMERS AND RAW GEORGIA WINTERS.

THAT A SCAR MAY BE NO MORE THAN THE WATER LIE SHIMMER OFF AUGUST BLACKTOP, HEAT LIGHTNING, AND WORSE THAN THAT, WORSE THAN THE LIE OF HEALING,,,

,,,A PUCKERED FLESH REMINDER OF THE SECOND BEFORE THE BLADE TOUCHED SKIN, ALL THE LINEN CLEAN MOMENTS BEFORE THE STAIN.

SUMMER 1986 AND FIVE BOYS, FIVE DEATHS IN FOUR STICKY, CRICKET WHISPER NIGHTS; THE GRAVES WERE FILLED IN A LONG, LONG TIME AGO, AND DAY STILL FOLLOWS NIGHT HERE, BUT THE CLOCK'S STOPPED, ANYWAY.

SO MUCH CRAZY HURT IN SO LITTLE SPACE AND TIME CAN WRINKLE A GOOD PLACE AND IT ISN'T THAT THERE ARE GHOSTS,,,

,,,NO WANDERING PHANTOM SHEETS AND MIDNIGHT SOBBING, NO CHAIN-RATTLE SPIRITS NAILED TO EARTH-- THE GHOSTED MINDS OF THE LIVING, THOUGH, THE HAUNTED LEFT-BEHINDS.

AND A GOOD PLACE (OR AT LEAST A NOT-BAD PLACE) TURNS INTO A BRUISE.

FIVE BOYS IN FOUR RED NIGHTS, FROM A TOWN WHERE PEOPLE STILL SLEPT WITH DOORS UN-LOCKED AND TALKED TO STRANGERS. THE SCARS ARE PLAIN TO SEE.

AND THE BEAST COME BACK AROUND.

DON'T GUESS THIS PLACE HAS CHANGED A WHOLE HECK OF A LOT. WELL, NOT SINCE LINCOLN WAS PRESIDENT, ANYWAY.

I WOULDN'T KNOW.

SO, WHAT NOW? YOU THINK THIS IS WHERE IT'S COMING FROM?

HEY. YOU FEELING OKAY?

DÉJÀ VU. I THINK.

OOOH. I HATE THAT.

JONATHAN HOWARD THAYER
1969 — 1986
Sanctuary in Paradise

NOT HERE, BUT I THINK I KNOW WHERE TO LOOK, NOW. AND I NEED TO DO THIS ALONE.

LUCIEN SAID...

I DON'T CARE WHAT THE BOOKWORM SAID. DON'T PISS ME OFF, BIRDIE. I'M NOT GOING FAR. AND I'LL BE BACK.

WELL...

DAMN.

You're a raven?

NO, I'M A DAMN CANARY. WHAT'S IT TO YOU?

The kudzu lady *said* there was gonna be a raven. I never met a raven before.

WELL NOW YOU HAVE. CONGRATULATIONS.

The kudzu lady was talking about *him*, too. Except she made him sound a lot bigger. Is he a friend of yours?

UH... SOMETHING LIKE THAT. THIS LADY, SHE TALKS TO BIRDS?

Mostly.

AND SHE KNEW WE WERE COMING?

Well, she said there'd be a raven, and a... him. You're lots bigger than I thought you'd be.

I THINK I SHOULD TALK TO HER.

She said you'd say that.

JEEZ, WHAT A DUMP. *THIS* IS HER HOUSE?

Most of the time...

Hello?

GOOD EVENIN', BLACKBIRD. YOU FOUND HIM.

He was in the cemetery, and the other one was there, too. But he left.

HOW YOU DOIN' TONIGHT, RAVENBIRD?

UM, KINDA CONFUSED, NOW THAT YOU ASK, WHO TOLD YOU WE WERE COMING?

I THOUGHT MAYBE YOU'D BE HUNGRY, SO I PICKED SOMETHING UP. I DON'T RECKON IT'S BEEN DEAD TOO LONG.

I THINK A TRUCK OR A CAR MUST'A HIT IT, BUT IT AIN'T TOO MASHED UP OR NOTHIN'. NOT IF YOU'RE HUNGRY.

YOU DIDN'T HAVE TO DO THAT.

YOU'RE THE ONE COME FOR GABE ASHE, AIN'T YOU? YOU AND THE MAN WITH SMILIN' EYES.

UH, YEAH, I THINK SO.

YOU *SEE*, BLACKBIRD? I *TOLD* YOU SO. I SAID IF GABE ASHE AND THAT SISSY BOY OF HIS KEPT ON MESSIN' AROUND WITH ALL THAT WITCHY SHIT THEY WAS GONNA BRING HIM BACK HERE....

...AND I WAS *RIGHT*, WASN'T I, RAVENBIRD?

WELL, NOT EXACTLY, BUT PROBABLY CLOSE ENOUGH.

SO *YOU* JUST *REMEMBER* THAT, MR. WINK-WINK-SHE'S-CRAZY-AS-A-JUNEBUG-IN-NOVEMBER, MR. HIGH-AND-MIGHTY BLACKBIRD.

SO, WHO'S THIS GABE ASHE GUY?

DON'T YOU ALREADY **KNOW**? DIDN'T **HE** TELL YOU?

GABRIEL ASHE. HE GOT A VISIT FROM THE MAN WITH SMILIN' EYES LAST TIME, ONLY HE DIDN'T DIE, LIKE ALL THE REST.

HIM AND ME, WE WERE THE ONLY ONES THAT SAW THE MAN AND LIVED TO TELL. BUT HE GOT GABE'S EYEBALLS.

NO...

HE'S A **FAGGOT**, YOU KNOW.

UH, **WHO'S** A FAGGOT?

THAT GABE ASHE, **THAT'S** WHO, AND THAT CITYTRASH BOYCHILD THAT HE BROUGHT BACK WITH HIM FROM ATLANTA, THAT SPOOKY ONE THAT DRESSES IN WOMEN'S CLOTHES AND LIKE HE WAS ALWAYS ON HIS WAY TO A FUNERAL.

THEY DON'T **KNOW** I WATCH THEM, BUT I **DO**, RAVEN. I STILL GOT **MY** EYES.

I THINK MAYBE I BETTER GO NOW. BUT THANKS FOR THE RABBIT.

YEAH, WELL, YOU TELL HIM I SAID THEY **BOTH** GOT WHATEVER HE'S GONNA DO COMIN' TO 'EM. THEY SPIT AT ME.

AND TELL HIM I'M READY WHENEVER IT'S MY TURN. I MISS JOHNNY, AND NOBODY LIKES ME ANYWAY. YOU TELL HIM THAT FOR ME, RAVENBIRD.

JOHNNY?

HE DOESN'T TELL YOU **NOTHIN'** DOES HE?

NO, BUT I REALLY KINDA PREFER IT THAT WAY.

WELL, JOHNNY **THAYER**, MY **BROTHER**, THAT'S WHO. THE MAN'LL REMEMBER HIM. JOHNNY HAD EYES THE COLOR OF THE SKY RIGHT BEFORE A SUMMER THUNDERSTORM. HE'LL REMEMBER.

ATLANTA.

MALL ENTRANCE

THIS IS A *VERY* BAD IDEA, GABE. WE'RE STILL WAY TOO CLOSE TO THE CLUB ...

GABRIEL! CHRIST, WAIT ...

POOR BABY. I KNOW IT'S TERRIBLE, I KNOW IT'S SO HARD ON YOU.

YOU DON'T *KNOW,* YOU DON'T FUCKING KNOW HIS HANDS, HIS FACE AND WHAT HE SAID ...

IT HURTS, ECHO. GOD IT *HURTS* AND YOU DON'T HAVE ANY FUCKING IDEA HOW *SCARED* ...

AND THEN HE'S GOING DOWN ...

DOWN TO THE RESTLESS, SHIFTING PLACE THAT TASTES LIKE CHIMNEY CINDERS AND BILE, SWEAT-STINK AND BLEACH, AND THE MONSTER IS OUTSIDE AGAIN, WANTING IN AND GABRIEL'S ALONE IN THE HOUSE WHERE HIS GRANDMOTHER DIED.

PIGGY? YOU IN THERE, BOY?

OF THE FIVE HE WAS THE LAST, AND THE ONLY ONE WHO WAS AT HOME.

SAFE HERE, GABE, SHE SAID, YOU'LL *ALWAYS* BE SAFE IN THIS HOUSE, CHILD, THIS HOUSE THAT DONE COME THROUGH SO MUCH FIRE AND HURT...

scritch scritch

OPEN THE *DOOR*, BOY. OPEN THIS DOOR AND LET ME IN.

THIS OLD HOUSE SAFE AS IF IT WAS BUILT FROM BRICKS AND NO PHONE, THOUGH, AND IT WAS ALREADY LATE SUMMER, DOG DAYS AND NO SCHOOL TO BRING HIM INTO TOWN WHERE HE MIGHT HAVE HEARD WHAT WAS HAPPENING.

I CAN *GET IN*, PIGGY. I CAN LET MYSELF IN *ANY TIME* I WANT, SO YOU'RE JUST WASTING OUR TIME.

CRASH

scritch

SHHHH, ANGEL. IT'S JUST *YOU* AND *ME* NOW, JUST YOU AND ME AND THERE'S NOTHING OUT THERE *HALF* AS BAD AS YOU.

THE NIGHTMARE KNOWS EXACTLY WHERE HE'S GOING, AS IF HE'S WALKED THIS ROAD BEFORE. WHICH *HE* HASN'T. NOT *HIS* MEMORIES DRAWN FROM *HIS* EXPERIENCES, BUT MEMORIES NONETHELESS.

THERE'S NO DOUBT WHAT HE'LL FIND.

HE'S SPENT SO MUCH TIME ON DREAD, THE INEVITABLE POINT OF CONTACT BETWEEN PAST DEEDS AND PRESENT FEAR, THAT THESE FINAL STEPS ARE RELEASE...

ASHE

AND FINALLY, THE SIGHT OF THIS HOUSE IS STRANGE RELIEF.

POLICE DO NOT CROSS

HELLO?

CLIK

UHM.... I'M BACK.

....HE SAYS AND OF COURSE THERE'S NO RESPONSE (HE KNEW THERE WOULDN'T BE), BUT IT BREAKS THE CICADA-RIDDLED STILLNESS, THE STIFLING QUIET, AND HE CAN'T HELP BUT SMILE.

SCREEUNK

WHAT HE *DOESN'T* KNOW IS EXACTLY WHAT HE'LL FIND HERE.

WHETHER IT WOULD ALL GO DOWN HERE, OR IF HE'D BE TOO LATE. IF THE GHOSTS WOULD BE WAITING...

...OPEN ARMS OR BARED TEETH FOR THE PRODIGAL.

AND NOW IT'S PRETTY CLEAR...

...HE'S MISSED THE PARTY ALTOGETHER.

NOTHING LEFT HERE BUT IMPRESSIONS, LINGERING LIKE STALE CIGARETTE SMOKE IN A BAR OR THE SHELLSHOCK CALM THAT FOLLOWS THUNDER.

BUT SOME IMPRESSIONS ARE DEEPER THAN OTHERS.

THERE YOU ARE, YOU SMUG SON-OF-A-BITCH.

DO YOU WANNA HEAR ABOUT HOW SICK I AM OF YOU, HOW SICK I AM OF WALKING IN YOUR FOOTSTEPS?

I DIDN'T THINK SO.

END OF PART ONE —

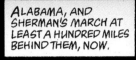
ALABAMA, AND SHERMAN'S MARCH AT LEAST A HUNDRED MILES BEHIND THEM, NOW.

GABRIEL ASHE WAKES UP AND JUST LIKE EVERY TIME BEFORE, HE WONDERS AND WISHES FOR A FEW SLEEP-FOGGED SECONDS THAT IT MIGHT HAVE BEEN A DREAM.

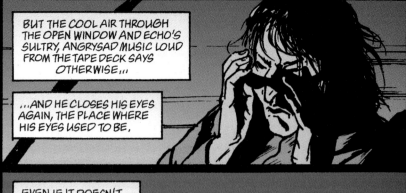
BUT THE COOL AIR THROUGH THE OPEN WINDOW AND ECHO'S SULTRY, ANGRYSAD MUSIC LOUD FROM THE TAPE DECK SAYS OTHERWISE...

...AND HE CLOSES HIS EYES AGAIN, THE PLACE WHERE HIS EYES USED TO BE,

EVEN IF IT DOESN'T MAKE A DIFFERENCE.

HANG ON, BABY, WE'RE GONNA MAKE A LITTLE STOP.

WHAT'S WRONG?

NOTHING'S WRONG, GABE. SOMEBODY JUST NEEDS A RIDE.

SOUVENIRS
part two

Caitlín R. Kiernan, writer
Peter Doherty, artist
Todd Klein, letterer
Daniel Vozzo, colorist & seps
Jennifer Lee, assistant editor
Alisa Kwitney, editor
Neil Gaiman, consultant

THE DREAMING created by Neil Gaiman

YOU KNOW, AFTER YOU'VE HAD A FEW OF THESE THINGS, THE NOVELTY KINDA STARTS TO WEAR THIN.

YOU WANT THE EYES? THEY'RE PRETTY SHRIVELED UP...

...AND THE ANTS HAVE BEEN AT THEM ALREADY...

NO ONE WANTS A BIG, BLACK, SMELLY BIRD IN THEIR CAR. I OUGHT TO JUST MAKE YOU FLY.

OH YEAH, AND YOU'RE MR. CONGENIALITY?

I DON'T THINK YOU EVEN KNOW WHERE WE'RE GOING, DO YOU?

GET OUT OF THE ROAD, RAVEN. THERE'S ANOTHER CAR COMING.

BIRMINGHAM? SURE, THAT WOULD BE GREAT.

OH MAN, WOW! A PET CROW, JUST LIKE THE GUY IN THAT MOVIE...

OH... YEAH, HE'S A SWEETIE.

YOU TEACH HIM TO SAY ANYTHING?

NO, THAT'S ONLY MYNAH BIRDS AND PARROTS. RAVENS JUST AREN'T THAT SMART.

BIRMINGHAM, ALABAMA.

SCRATCH THE SURFACE OF THIS PLACE AND THE BONES OF THE WORLD ARE IRON.

RED ORE SKELETON BORN IN PALEOZOIC SEAS, BURIED HERE FOUR HUNDRED MILLION YEARS TO STAIN THE SOIL LIKE BLOOD.

ORE MINED FOR THE BIG FURNACES DURING THE LONG DECADES OF SMOKE-GRAY DAYS AND FIRE-COLORED NIGHTS,...

...THE ROLLING STEEL AGE OF INDUSTRY AND PROGRESS THAT SEEMS AS MUCH A GHOST NOW AS THE WARM WATERS OF ANCIENT OCEANS.

THE PILLS MIGHT HAVE WORN OFF, OR SHE MIGHT BE DEAD BY NOW. IT'S HOT,...

SHE ISN'T DEAD, GABRIEL.

WAKE UP, BITCH.

RIDE'S OVER.

THE VOICE IN HIS HEAD LIKE HONEY ON BROKEN GLASS, SWEET AND RAZOR SHARP VOICE HE NO LONGER KNOWS IF HE'S REMEMBERING...

...OR IF IT'S JUST HIS OWN.

THE RULE INSIDE THE IDIOT RHYME, "THE EYES OF BOYS ARE PRETTY THINGS, SAVORY LUSCIOUS FARE..."

"...BUT I'D NEVER TASTE THE SIGHT OF GIRLS, EVEN ON A DARE."

ECHO?

ECHO? I'M COMING. I'M SORRY.

HE USED TO BE CERTAIN OF THE DIFFERENCE, THAT THERE HAD BEEN ANOTHER VOICE, A BEAUTIFUL MAN WHO'D COME FOR HIM, A MAN WITH EYES THAT SPOKE SO HIS BEAUTIFUL LIPS COULD DO OTHER THINGS.

A MAN WHO TOLD HIM HE WASN'T THE FREAK, THAT IT WASN'T WRONG TO FEEL THE THINGS HE FELT.

THAP

ECHO! I'M SORRY, OKAY? I CAN'T FIND YOU...

BUT THE MAN MIGHT HAVE BEEN A DREAM.

I'M OVER HERE, GABE. TO YOUR RIGHT.

JESUS, ECHO, DON'T DO THAT. *PLEASE* DON'T DO THAT.

I THOUGHT YOU WERE BEHIND ME, BABY. I *SWEAR*, I THOUGHT YOU WERE RIGHT THERE BEHIND ME.

I REALLY WISH YOU COULD SEE THIS PLACE, GABRIEL. IT'S LIKE SOMETHING OUT OF A RIDLEY SCOTT MOVIE, OR A GIGER PAINTING.

IT'D BE A FABULOUS PLACE FOR A RAVE. JUST PUT IN SOME LIGHTS AND A SOUND SYSTEM.

INDUSTRIAL, GOTH, TECHNO, TRANCE, *WHATEVER*... THIS PLACE WOULD BE THE SHIT.

SURE, IT'D TAKE SOME MONEY, I GUESS....

JESUS, BITCH, BE STILL! I ALMOST CUT MY FUCKING HAND.

HURRY, ECHO....

WE'RE HALFWAY THERE, BABY.

YEAH, I HAD A PARAKEET ONCE, YOU KNOW, BUT IT GOT OUT OF ITS CAGE AND MY GIRLFRIEND'S CAT ATE IT.

YOU CAN LET US OUT HERE.

HERE?

THERE AIN'T NOTHING OUT HERE...

JUST STOP THE BLOODY CAR!

SURE, MAN. WHATEVER YOU SAY.

WHAT WAS *THAT* ABOUT? I MEAN, YEAH, THE KID WAS DRIVING ME NUTS, TOO, BUT THERE REALLY *IS* NOTHING OUT HERE. *LOTS* OF IT, TOO.

HE'S *CLOSE*, RAVEN. SOMEWHERE CLOSE.

HOW THE HELL DO YOU *KNOW* THAT? IT WOULDN'T HURT YOU TO TELL ME A FEW OF THESE THINGS.

HOW *DO YOU* KNOW WHEN LUCIEN WANTS TO TALK TO YOU?

HOW'D YOU KNOW YOU NEEDED TO LEAVE ME *STRANDED* AT SWARTALF-HEIM SO YOU COULD HANG OUT WITH EVERY OTHER WORTHLESS SACK OF GREASY BLACK FEATHERS IN THE WORLD?

VRROOM

UM, WELL, I JUST...WELL, YOU KNOW...

OKAY. I KINDA SEE WHAT YOU MEAN.

STOP IT! WE CANNOT LEAVE THAT GIRL ALIVE. SHE *SAW* US. SHE SAW US BOTH.

HE'S COMING, ECHO.

LET ME GO!

WHO'S COMING, GABRIEL? WHO THE HELL DO YOU THINK IS COMING?

THE MAN. THE ONE WHO CAME TO...

OH, THAT'S A LOAD OF HORSESHIT AND YOU DAMN WELL KNOW IT.

I *KILL* FOR YOU, GABE. I KILL FOR YOU BECAUSE I LOVE YOU AND I KNOW YOU NEED IT. AND BECAUSE IT'S SUCH A FUCKING *THRILL...*

...BUT I'M NOT LEAVING A WITNESS JUST BECAUSE YOU THINK...

THNAK!

YOU'RE GONNA *DO* WHAT I *SAY*. YOU DON'T HAVE ANY FUCKING IDEA WHAT'S REALLY GOING ON HERE. THIS ISN'T SOME KIND OF GODDAMN GAME...

GET UP, ECHO. WE HAVE TO GET OUT OF HERE.

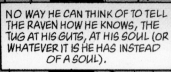

NO WAY HE CAN THINK OF TO TELL THE RAVEN HOW HE KNOWS, THE TUG AT HIS GUTS, AT HIS SOUL (OR WHATEVER IT IS HE HAS INSTEAD OF A SOUL).

BUT SOME LINK BETWEEN HIM AND THIS HUMAN, BOND AS REAL AS AN UMBILICAL CORD, AS VITAL AS FLESH OR BLOOD, MENTAL SOUVENIR OR SCAR FROM SOMETHING HE DID BEFORE HE WAS EVEN ALIVE.

AND THE NIGHTMARE KNOWS THAT HE'S MISSED THE BOY AGAIN.

THEY'VE GONE ALREADY...

YOU NOTICED THAT, DID YOU? SMART BIRDIE.

JESUS. ANOTHER ONE. IS SHE DEAD?

NO, RAVEN. THIS ONE'S STILL ALIVE.

AND SHE STILL HAS ONE EYE LEFT.

WE OUGHTA GET HER SOME KIND OF HELP.

UM...

I MEAN, GET HER TO A HOSPITAL....

...RIGHT?

YEAH. WE COULD DO THAT.

SHE'S LOST AN EYE AND A LOT OF BLOOD....THERE'S PROBABLY STILL TIME TO SAVE HER LIFE.

BUT WHAT KIND OF LIFE DO YOU THINK SHE'D BE LIKELY TO HAVE AFTER THIS, HMM?

I MEAN, LOOK HOW WELL MR. GABRIEL ASHE HAS MADE THE ADJUSTMENT.

SOMEONE DID HIM A BIG FAVOR, STITCHING HIM BACK TOGETHER, DIDN'T THEY? DID US ALL A FAVOR, HM?

JESUS. YOU GOTTA BE KIDDIN'.

WHY? IT'S THE ONLY MERCIFUL THING *TO DO.*

THAT'S *BULLSHIT* AND YOU *KNOW* IT.

THE *TRUTH* IS YOU *WANT* TO *KILL* THIS GIRL AND EAT HER EYE.

EITHER WAY, IT'S NO CONCERN OF YOURS.

THERE'S NO WAY I'M JUST GONNA STAND HERE AND WATCH YOU KILL HER.

ACTUALLY, THERE'S NO WAY YOU CAN STOP ME.

YOU'VE HAD YOUR *CARRION,* LITTLE BIRD, AND NOW IT'S MY TURN!

SO DON'T *FUCK* WITH ME!

...BETTER HOPE SHE DIES BEFORE ANYONE FINDS HER, GABE.

'CAUSE I AM *NOT* GOING TO JAIL BE-CAUSE YOU'RE TOO CHICKENSHIT... CHRIST, I NEED A CIGARETTE.

WHAT ARE YOU *DOING*, GABE?

UNNNNNNHH...

THERE, ASSHOLE... SHE SAVED YOU THE TROUBLE.

SHE SAVED YOUR *LIFE*.

AND THAT'S *TWICE* NOW I SHOULD'VE KILLED YOU.

THIRD TIME'S THE CHARM...

NOT HERE, GABE! NO...

NOT IN THE *CAR*, YOU FUCKING PSYCHO!

THREE STRIKES, LITTLE BIRD...

"...YOU'RE OUT."

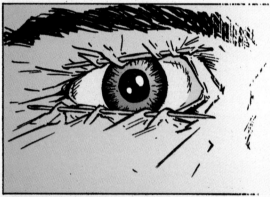

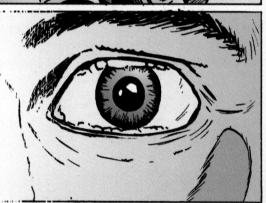

AND NEITHER OF THEM EXPECTED THIS.

HUNH?

GABE! WHAT? WHAT'S HAPPENING?

WHAT'S WRONG, BABY?

NO, GABE! STOP!

HEY. YOU OKAY?

SCREEE

YOU... WAIT...

GABE, SAY SOMETHING, PLEASE...

SHHHH...

YOU'RE ALL RIGHT, BABY. NOTHING'S GONNA HURT YOU NOW.

WHAT THE HECK WAS THAT?

ASSHOLE.

TWO DAYS LATER. THE FRENCH QUARTER, NEW ORLEANS.

MUGGY SLOW CITY THAT SMELLS LIKE SOMETHING THAT'S FORGOTTEN HOW TO DIE.

ECHO TALKING. ECHO ALWAYS TALKING NOW, ALWAYS EXCITED AND GABRIEL HEARS THE WORDS BUT CAN'T REALLY STRING THEM INTO MEANING.

EVEN WHEN HE TRIES.

♪ ...THAT SAVED A WRETCH LIKE ME. I ONCE WAS LOST, BUT NOW I'M FOUND... ♪♫

♪ ...WAS BLIND, BUT NOW I SEE. ♫♪

C'MON, GABE. IT'S GETTING DARK. WE'LL BE LATE...

ECHO'S PLAN, ECHO'S SPELL, SOMETHING FROM ONE OF HIS MUSTY OLD BOOKS, MOLDY, SILVERFISH STACKS OF THEM BACK IN THEIR HOUSE IN SHERMAN'S MARCH. ALL HE'S TALKED ABOUT SINCE BIRMINGHAM.

YOU CAN'T SCREW AROUND WITH THESE PEOPLE. THEY'RE DOING *US* A FAVOR, EVEN DEALING WITH US.

A BINDING, ECHO SAID, TO HOLD THIS THING, TO WEAKEN IT. A HEART FOR ITS PURPOSE, EYES FOR ITS VISION...

SHIT. GABRIEL CAN NEVER REMEMBER IT ALL.

ECHO'S TRAP FOR SOMETHING HE DOESN'T EVEN BEGIN TO COMPREHEND...

BUT THERE'S ALWAYS THE SLIM CHANCE THAT ECHO'S RIGHT, CLEVER BY ACCIDENT, AND THIS THING HE MEANS TO DO *MIGHT* BUY GABRIEL A LITTLE MORE TIME.

MORE TIME TO PRETEND...

THE RAGGED WALLS BETWEEN THIS WORLD AND GABRIEL'S NIGHTMARES ARE RAVELING, WISPTHIN VEIL BETWEEN WHO HE IS NOW AND SOMEONE HE MIGHT HAVE BEEN TEN YEARS BEFORE.

JESUS, GABE. WHAT IF WE'VE MISSED THEM?

I MEAN, YOU UNDER-STAND WE'RE NOT GONNA FIND SOMEONE WITH THIS SORT OF MERCHAN-DISE ON EVERY STREET CORNER.

IT'S NOT LIKE BUYING DOPE OR SOMETHING.

HE'S BEEN PLAYING A GAME OF HIS MEMORIES, GAME OF IDENTITY AND CONSE-QUENCE, AND HE *ALMOST* KNOWS THAT NOW.

SHIT.

FORGIVE MY TARDINESS, *MADAM.* THERE WAS AN UN-FORTUNATE DELAY ...

OH ...NO, UM, NO PROBLEM AT ALL, REALLY.

NO, IT'S QUITE UNFORGIVABLE, MY MISTRESS SENDS HER DEEPEST APOLOGIES ...

I TRUST YOU HAVE THE *ITEM* SHE DISCUSSED WITH YOU?

YES, OF COURSE. IT'S RIGHT HERE.

VERY GOOD, THEN.

IT'S A PLEASURE TO DO BUSINESS WITH TWO SUCH RESPONSIBLE YOUNG PEOPLE.

YEAH, THANKS ....

YOU'D BE SURPRISED HOW MANY SHOW UP EMPTY-HANDED, OR DON'T BOTHER SHOWING UP AT ALL.

AH, YES. PERFECT.

MY MISTRESS ASSURES YOU, IT'S BEEN HER PLEASURE, AND SHE CAUTIONS YOU, CHILD...

THIS IS SERIOUS BUSINESS.

WATCH YOURSELVES.

JESUS. I THINK MAYBE I PEED ON MYSELF.

IS IT WHAT YOU NEEDED?

YEAH, GABE. THIS IS IT, EXACTLY.

NOW THAT HE'S DONE HIS DUTY, NOW THAT THE BLIND BOY AND HIS STRANGE LOVER ARE BEHIND HIM, CLAUDE JOLICOEUR CAN ACKNOWLEDGE THE FEAR RUMBLING IN HIS BELLY.

SO MANY YEARS HE'S BEEN THE PERFECT SERVANT, ENTRUSTED BY HIS *HOUGAN* WITH THE MOST DELICATE AFFAIRS.

THE BAD MOTHERFUCKER THAT GETS THE JOB DONE, REGARDLESS.

NOTHING THE VOODOO WOMAN CAN'T TRUST HIM WITH, BUT THIS TIME HE SAW THE WORRY ON HER FACE.

AND NOW HE UNDERSTANDS.

IT'S *NOT* THE FACT THAT THEY ARE KILLERS.

THOSE TWO, TOUCHED BY SOMETHING BLACK AND MORE POWERFUL THAN ANY *GRIS-GRIS*.

ALREADY, THE MAGIC THEY PLOT AGAINST IT IS IRRELEVANT.

ALREADY LOST, LIKE A CLEAN DROP OF SUMMER RAIN IN A MUDDY, FLOOD-SWOLLEN RIVER.

THIS DARK NIGHT IS FULL OF SPIRITS, BAD DREAMS AND OLD HARM DRESSED UP IN THE DECEITFUL SKINS OF MEN.

CLAUDE JOLICOEUR WHISPERS TO THE KINDERGODS, AND HE HURRIES HOME.

WHEN I WAS A LITTLE BOY I HAD A DREAM...

I WAS IN HEAVEN AND IT WAS FULL OF PAGANS, DANCING ROUND AND RAVISHING EACH OTHER'S NAKED BODIES...

YOU'RE DRUNK.

FRANKENSTEIN
MARY WOLLSTONECRAFT SHELLEY

AND THEN I WENT TO HELL AND IT WAS FULL OF ANGELS...

...ANGELS IN HELL, DOING GOOD THINGS.

TO BE CONCLUDED.

DECATUR STREET, THE FRENCH QUARTER, NEW ORLEANS.

OFF THE MUGGY, STINKING STREET AND UP THESE STAIRS TO A SHABBY SANCTUARY OF NOISE AND SMOKE ABOVE.

SAFER HAVEN FOR THE THIN CHILDREN WHO PAINT THEIR FACES WHITE, SMUDGE EYES BLACK WITH CHEAP MAKEUP.

NO, MAN. THIS SHIT'S *BETTER* THAN X, I SWEAR.

SICK OR BORED ENOUGH WITH LIFE AND LIGHT, THEY COURT DEATH AND DARKNESS.

SELF-STYLED CHILDREN OF THE NIGHT AND CLUELESS POSEURS AND FERVENT WANNABES.

PAIN AND FASHION AND CALCULATED DESPAIR.

CAN WE GO BACK IN NOW? *PLEASE?* I WANT TO DANCE...

STABBING MARY

STABBING MARY

FaLLING JaNUS & DEATH'S LITTLE SISTER
One Nite Only

FALLING JANUS AND DEATH'S LITTLE SISTER! ONE NITE ONLY

ALL OF THEM SO BUSY WITH THEIR OWN NIGHTMARES, ACTUAL AND ASSUMED, THAT THEY DON'T SEE THE REAL THING WHEN IT WALKS THROUGH THE DOOR.

SOUVENIRS
part three

Caitlín R. Kiernan, writer
Peter Doherty, artist
D'Israeli, artist
Todd Klein, letterer
Daniel Vozzo, colorist & seps
Jennifer Lee, assistant editor
Alisa Kwitney, editor
Neil Gaiman, consultant

THE DREAMING created by Neil Gaiman

JEEZ, WHAT A RACKET.

SHUT UP. SOMEONE'S GOING TO HEAR YOU.

YOU CAN TELL 'EM YOU'RE A VENTRILOQUIST.

ANYWAY, NO ONE'S GONNA HEAR *ANYTHING* OVER ALL THIS NOISE. I CAN'T EVEN HEAR MYSELF THINK.

WHAT'LL YOU... *HEY,* WHO SAID YOU COULD BRING THAT *BIRD* IN HERE?

OH, I DON'T GO *ANYWHERE* WITHOUT HIM THESE DAYS. HE'S MY LITTLE BUDDY.

HEY, *I* COULDN'T CARE LESS, BUT IT'S GONNA BE *MY* BUTT THAT GETS CHEWED OUT IF HE CRAPS ON ANYONE.

DON'T WORRY ABOUT THAT. HE'S *HOUSEBROKEN.* AREN'T YOU, BIRDIE?

THE HEART IS ONLY HALF THE PHYSICAL CATALYST, GABE. WE STILL NEED TWO EYES.

IT'S NOT A DIFFICULT SPELL, BUT IT'S POWERFUL, AND EVERYTHING HAS TO BE PERFECT. WE'LL NEED TIME AND A PLACE WE WON'T BE DISTURBED.

WHEN THE BINDING IS DONE, ALL HIS SECRETS, ALL HIS *POWER*, EVERYTHING HE *IS*, WILL BE OURS, GABE.

SOMETIMES YOU SOUND LIKE YOU'RE MAKING FUN OF ME, LIKE YOU'RE MAKING THIS WHOLE THING UP AS YOU GO ALONG.

I'M NOT MAKING *"FUN"* OF YOU.

THAT WAS A DAMNED STUPID THING TO SAY.

"ALL HIS POWER WILL BE OURS." YOU SOUND FUCKING RIDICULOUS.

YOU KNOW THAT, DON'T YOU? YOU SOUND LIKE A GODDAMNED COMIC BOOK.

THIS ISN'T EVEN ABOUT *YOU!* THIS IS BETWEEN ME AND HIM.

I REALLY DON'T NEED YOU, ECHO...

GABRIEL, STOP...

OH GOD...

NO, GODDAMNIT! THIS TIME YOU'RE GOING TO LISTEN.

HE'S *HERE*, GABE. AT THE BAR, *JESUS...* HE'S REAL.

BULLSHIT. I DIDN'T FEEL HIM COMING...

MAYBE YOU WERE TOO BUSY *TALKING* TO NOTICE. NOW JUST MOVE YOUR ASS, BOYFRIEND.

I THINK I HAVE TO PISS.

YOU DO THAT?

I'VE NEVER HAD TO BEFORE, BUT I THINK I HAVE TO NOW.

HEY, WATCH IT!

HEAD

I GUESS I'M ABOUT TO FIND OUT, THOUGH, ONE WAY OR ANOTHER. YOU COMING WITH ME?

WOULDN'T MISS IT FOR THE WORLD.

LOCK IT.

THERE'S NO LOCK ...THERE'S NOT A LOCK ON THIS FUCKING DOOR.

I'M NOT READY FOR THIS, GABE. WE NEEDED TIME TO PREPARE. SOMEPLACE PRIVATE, AND WE STILL HAVE TO GET THE EYES...

WE HAVE THE EYES, ECHO.

HEY, *YOU'RE* THAT GUY, AREN'T YOU? THAT GUY IN THAT BAND FROM, UM, YOU KNOW. YOU'RE *HIM*.

HEAD

COOL BIRD!

CHRIST...

WHOA, DID THAT BIRD JUST SAY SOMETHING?

UH, NO. LOOK, I HAVE TO...

IT *DID*, IT JUST SAID "CHRIST."

YOU SURE AS HELL *LOOK* LIKE HIM.

GABE, PLEASE ...

I *SWEAR*, YOU LOOK *JUST* LIKE HIM.

PINHEADS.

SEE? HE DID IT AGAIN.

EXCUSE ME...

I AM VERY SORRY. I NEVER MEANT FOR YOU TO GET HURT...

AND THERE ARE VOICES, THEN, VOICES OUTSIDE THE DOOR, AND SO HE HURRIES,

AND IN HURRYING, FORGETS THEIR PRIZE, COLD MEAT AND SHARP WIRE TWISTS ...BUT IT'S NOT IMPORTANT.

HE ISN'T TAKING THE EYE FOR ECHO'S SPELL,...

HE'S INVENTED HIS OWN TRICK.

FLOP

WE'RE WASTING TIME.

YEAH, WELL, COMIN' TO THIS JOINT WAS YOUR IDEA.

PERHAPS I WAS WRONG.

YEAH, WELL, NOBODY'D LIKE THAT MORE THAN ME...

BUT MAYBE YOU OUGHTA GET A LOOK AT THIS BEFORE WE THROW A PARTY.

UNGH....

JESUS, GABRIEL MADE YOU SOUND A WHOLE HELL OF A LOT BIGGER ...

WHERE IS HE?

GONE. HE'S JUST GONE.

WHERE HAS HE GONE? I DON'T HAVE TIME TO PLAY GAMES WITH YOU.

GET BENT.

YEAH, YOU TAKE IT. GO AHEAD. YOU REALLY THINK I GIVE A SHIT ANYMORE?

GO ON! IT'S WHAT HE WANTED YOU TO DO. IT'S WHAT YOU'RE SUPPOSED TO DO, YOU STUPID, PREDICTABLE BASTARD.

WHAT'S SHE .... UH, HE TALKING ABOUT?

AND WHAT IS THAT?

THAT, BIRDIE, WAS A LITTLE SURPRISE THE KIDDIES HAD WAITING FOR ME.

WOULD IT HAVE WORKED?

MAYBE. MAYBE *NOT.* THAT SORT OF DEPENDS ON HOW MUCH BRIGHTER THIS LITTLE BOY IS THAN HE LOOKS.

BUT I THINK *NOT...*

YOU HAVE NO IDEA WHAT'S AT STAKE, WHAT I...

I DON'T KNOW *WHAT* YOU ARE, BUT I KNOW YOU'RE NOT INVINCIBLE.

SURELY YOU KNOW THAT. THERE ARE WAYS OF HOLDING *ANYTHING.*

YOU TAKE IT AND DO WHATEVER IT IS YOU DO, FIND HIM, AND GET THIS OVER WITH.

ONE WAY OR ANOTHER, END IT.

NO! WAIT! DON'T YOU *SEE* WHAT'S HAPPENING?

CUT HIM AND YOU'RE NO BETTER THAN THE FIRST CORINTHIAN.

I NEVER SAID I WAS BETTER THAN *ANYONE,* RAVEN.

THERE ARE THINGS I *NEED.*

YOU THINK YOU'RE THE ONLY ONE THAT EVER GOT HUNGRY? IF THE FIRST OF YOU SPOOKY FUCKS HAD SHOWN A LITTLE SELF-CONTROL NONE OF THIS WOULD HAVE HAPPENED!

IF *I'D* SHOWN A LITTLE WHEN I WAS ALIVE, I MIGHT STILL BE A MAN.

THE DREAMING.

HE KNOWS, NOW, THAT HE NEVER
INTENDED TO COME BACK HERE. HAD
MEANT ONLY TO FIND THE IMPOSTOR,
AND THAT LAST DUTY PERFORMED,
CALL IT EVEN; BUT HERE HE IS, LOYAL
HORROR, ALLEGIANT PHANTOM.

GOOD MONSTER.

AND KNOWING THAT HE HAD
A CHOICE DOESN'T REALLY
MAKE MUCH OF A DIFFERENCE.

NOT MUCH OF
A DIFFERENCE
AT ALL.

GET OUTTA THE DAMNED ROAD, YOU FUCKIN' CRACKHEAD!

HONK

HEY! YOU WIPE YER FEET NEXT TIME, YOU HEAR?

HE MISSES ECHO ALREADY. BUT THAT DOESN'T MEAN HE *NEEDS* ECHO.

CLICK

SCREEEK

THAT MUCH HE *DOES* UNDERSTAND. HIS OWN DARK TRICK.

OPEN WIDE....

A THIN PLACE, THE LIBRARIAN TOLD THE RAVEN. THIS FLAW BETWEEN WORLDS, SHRINKING NOW, EVAPORATING.

THERE'S PROBABLY A WORD FOR THIS IN ONE OF LUCIEN'S BOOKS, BUT IF THERE IS, THE NIGHTMARE DOESN'T KNOW IT.

SOMETHING SUCCINCT, ONE ECONOMICAL SYNONYM FOR "CLOSURE."

COME ON, BOY. I'M WAITING FOR YOU.

AND WITH THESE SMALL RIPPLES, SLEEPER'S HAND PLUNGED INTO A COLD AND BURNING POOL, THE DREAMQUAKE BEGINS.

THE CONSEQUENCE, FINALLY, SPREADING FROM ONE WORLD TO ANOTHER AND IT ROLLS LIKE VOICELESS THUNDER.

THE RIPPLES SPREAD, AND SOMETHING WITH VAST AND LEATHERY BAT WINGS FORGETS THE SMALL THING IT'S BEEN TORTURING AND STARES FEARFULLY TOWARD THE CORINTHIAN'S GLASSY PIT.

JUST BEYOND THE INDEFINITE BORDERS OF NIGHTMARE, A LOCOMOTIVE IS DERAILED MOMENTS BEFORE IT CAN BE ROBBED BY THE DREAMING INVESTMENT BANKER WAITING ON THE OTHER SIDE OF THE BRIDGE.

FARTHER OUT STILL, IN THE TALL AND RAMBLING HOUSE THAT HOLDS ALL THE UNIVERSE'S SECRETS, KITSCHY ARCANA AND DUSTY BRIC-A-BRAC TUMBLE NOISILY TO THE FLOOR.

IN HIS LIBRARY, THE LIBRARIAN OF BOOKS NEVER WRITTEN STEADIES A BOTTLE OF INK THE PRECISE COLOR OF THE SHADOWS BENEATH A FLOCK OF PTERODACTYLS.

MATTHEW?

AND HE COULD *STILL* WALK AWAY. ALLOW THE CARELESS SHOCK OF THIS VIOLATION TO TEAR A HOLE SO BIG THAT *TWO* WORLDS, A MILLION WORLDS, MIGHT SPILL IRREVOCABLY INTO ONE ANOTHER.

HE *COULD* LET THESE TREMORS GROW, AS MAD AS GABRIEL ASHE'S PAIN AND ANGER, AS WILD, UNTIL THERE'S NOTHING LEFT BUT THE SLUMBERING RUBBLE.

THERE'S NO ONE TO *FORCE* HIS HAND.

HE HAS A *CHOICE.*

HE WILL *ALWAYS* HAVE A CHOICE.

AND FACE TO FACE WITH THIS BOY, FINALLY. THIS BOY HE KNOWS, THOUGH THEY'VE NEVER MET. AND THE THINGS HE'S REMEMBERING THAT HE NEVER DID, THE SWEET, RED THINGS.

MEMORIES FROM ANOTHER LIFE, MEMORIES INHERITED LIKE THE COLOR OF HIS HAIR AND HIS APPETITES.

REMEMBERING, IN THIS PLACE THAT SMELLS LIKE COOKING AND DUST AND FEAR, THIS PLACE GONE AS STALE AS OLD BREAD, KEPT LIKE A PHOTOGRAPH OR A LEAF PRESSED BETWEEN YELLOWING PAGES, MENTAL KEEPSAKE SO A TERRIBLE HANDFUL OF MOMENTS CAN NEVER BE FORGOTTEN.

GABRIEL.

I HATE YOU, FUCKER.

SO WOUNDS CAN NEVER HEAL.

I THINK THAT'S THE WAY IT'S SUPPOSED TO WORK.

SONOFABITCH....

I ASSURE YOU, I DIDN'T HAVE A MOTHER OF ANY SORT.

YOU.... YOU THINK THIS IS FUNNY? YOU THINK THIS IS ALL SOME KIND OF GODDAMNED JOKE?

NO....

WELL, YES.... MAYBE I DO. JUST A LITTLE BIT.

I MEAN, THE WAY ALL THE SHIT IS *CONNECTED.* AN UNGUARDED NIGHTMARE GETS HORNY, GETS LOOSE AND STEALS THE EYES OF PRETTY YOUNG BOYS.

EXCEPT, PROBABLY BECAUSE HE'S SUCH A GENERAL FUCK-UP TO BEGIN WITH, HE FAILS TO *FINISH* THE JOB IN THIS ONE PAR-TICULAR CASE.

ONE LITTLE SHIT LEFT ALIVE IN EAST BUMBLEFUCK, GEOR-GIA...

ONE SORRY LITTLE SLIP OF A BOY WHO GETS IT IN HIS HEAD THAT IT'S EASIER TO HURT OTHERS THAN FEEL HIS *OWN* PAIN...

AND, OF COURSE, THIS SNOT HAS NO *IDEA* THAT HIS TORMENTOR WAS PUNISHED, PUNISHED *SEVERELY,* FOR HIS TRANSGRESSIONS...

NO IDEA THAT THE REST OF THE UNIVERSE HAS MOVED ON--BECAUSE IT'S SO MUCH *EASIER* TO PLAY PRETEND THAN JUST GET THE HELL *OVER* IT.

SO MUCH BETTER TO PRETEND HE'S THE *PREDATOR,* INSTEAD OF JUST ANOTHER ONE OF THE *VICTIMS...*

NO....

YES, GABRIEL. THAT'S PRECISELY WHAT YOU'VE DONE. BECAUSE IT FEELS SO MUCH BETTER, DOESN'T IT, BEING THE TIGER INSTEAD OF A COW...

...EVEN IF IT'S ONLY A *PAPER* TIGER.

JUST BETWEEN YOU AND ME, I DON'T CARE IF YOU'D RATHER HIDE FROM YOUR PROBLEMS. IT *WAS* SOME PRETTY UGLY SHIT, AND THAT'S *YOUR* BUSINESS.

NO, PLEASE...

AND HONESTLY, I CAN'T SAY I CARE ONE WAY OR ANOTHER ABOUT THE PEOPLE YOU'VE KILLED, EITHER...

I'M JUST NOT *MADE* THAT WAY.

UNFORTUNATELY, YOU'VE DRAGGED *ME* INTO YOUR CHARADE.

AND NOW THERE'S A LOT MORE AT STAKE THAN *EITHER* OF US.

SO, *THIS* TIME YOU'RE GOING TO LOOK, BOY, YOU'RE GOING TO KEEP YOUR EYES WIDE OPEN THROUGH ALL THE SCARY PARTS.

NO, I WON'T...

YES, GABRIEL. YES, YOU *WILL*. BECAUSE I'M SICK TO DEATH OF THIS SHIT...

I CAN'T...

....AND IT ENDS HERE, WHERE IT BEGAN.

...I CAN'T SEE.

OH, I THINK YOU CAN SEE JUST FINE.

WHICH IS A GOOD THING, GABRIEL, BECAUSE I WOULDN'T WANT YOU TO MISS ANYTHING.

IT'S SUCH A WONDERFUL GAME, AND I REALLY AM GOING TO NEED YOUR FULL ATTENTION.

HELP ME, PLEASE...

YOU KILLED ALL THOSE PEOPLE FOR HIM, DIDN'T YOU? HE COULDN'T HAVE DONE ALL THAT BY HIMSELF.

AT LEAST HE HAD AN EXCUSE. YOU'RE JUST A MURDERER.

WHY THE HELL SHOULD I HELP YOU?

SO WHY SHOULD I DO ANYTHING BUT STAND HERE AND WATCH YOU DIE.

BECAUSE... YOU'RE NOT LIKE HIM... YOU'RE GOOD, AREN'T YOU? YOU HAVE TO HELP...

WRONG. I'M NOT ANY BETTER THAN HE IS. THIS AIN'T ABOUT GOOD GUYS AND BAD GUYS.

I'M JUST A RAVEN, AND ALL I HAVE TO DO IS STAND HERE AND WAIT FOR YOU TO DIE. EAT A FEW BITES OF WHAT'S LEFT. THAT'S WHAT RAVENS DO.

OH, WOW...

YOU CAN TALK!

YEAH, SHERLOCK. I CAN TALK. I'M A TALKING BIRD. NOW, CALL HIM AN AMBULANCE OR I'M GONNA PECK YOUR STUPID FACE OFF.

HE HEARS THE LIBRARIAN, VOICE SHARP AND NEAT AS THE EDGES OF THE PAGES IN HIS BOOKS.

"MATTHEW?" THE VOICE ASKS, JUST ONCE, VERY QUIET AND A LITTLE FEAR SOMEWHERE UNDERNEATH.

HE'LL ANSWER, BECAUSE HE LIKES THE LIBRARIAN--LUCIEN, THE MAN WHO WAS THE VERY *FIRST* RAVEN--AND BECAUSE HE *NEEDS* TO BE NEEDED. NEEDS TO BE TRUSTED.

BUT FIRST THERE'S SOMETHING ELSE.

OVER SO FAST, CIRCLE CLOSED, AND HE SUSPECTS THIS IS THE PART WHERE HE SHOULD FEEL SATISFIED, FULFILLED, CERTAIN OF HIMSELF.

PROUD.

AFTER ALL, HE'S DONE HIS JOB. WHAT THE RAVEN WOULD HAVE SAID HE'D BEEN "MADE" TO DO.

IN THE END, GABRIEL ASHE SAW HIMSELF. COWERING, HELPLESS VICTIM, FACE SNIVELING BEHIND BLOOD AND TEARS AND HE KNEW THAT HE SAW THE TRUTH. ALL THE TRUTH THERE WAS TO SEE.

SAW HIMSELF, NOT THE THING THAT PUT HIM THERE, NOT SOMETHING STRONG AND SLEEK AND VICIOUS TO DOLE OUT DARK LIKE POISON CANDY TO NASTY CHILDREN.

BUT THE NIGHTMARE ONLY FEELS TIRED.

TIRED AND VERY HUNGRY.

HOW'D IT GO?

WHAT DO YOU WANT NOW?

UM, I JUST THOUGHT YOU MIGHT, UM,,, YOU KNOW.

NEED SOMEONE TO TALK TO.

NO, THERE'S NOTHING TO SAY.

OH,,,,

"Unkindness of One"

HE HAS THIS DREAM SOMETIMES.

HE'S HAVING IT NOW.

THIS DREAM, WHERE HE ISN'T A RAVEN ANYMORE, ISN'T A RAVEN *AGAIN* ...

AND HE'S REACHING *DOWN*, MAN'S ARM (FOR IN THIS DREAM HE *HAS* ARMS AGAIN) DOWN THROUGH THE WORLD AND PAIN AND TIME AND A DARKNESS THAT BURNS LIKE LIVING FIRE. ...

THIS DREAM WHERE HE'S SOMEONE HE'S ALMOST FORGOTTEN, OR *PRETENDS* HE'S ALMOST FORGOTTEN.

AND HIS ARMS ARE NEVER QUITE LONG ENOUGH.

SHHHHH. IT'S ALL RIGHT.

NOT EVEN SO CLOSE THAT THEIR FINGERS BRUSH, ONLY THE RAW SENSE OF REACHING, STRAINING AND *ALMOST...*

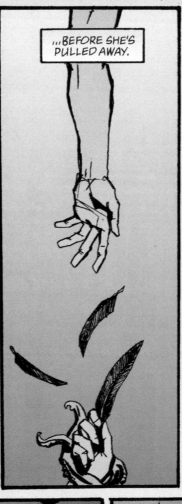

...BEFORE SHE'S PULLED AWAY.

AND THE RAVEN NAMED MATTHEW WAKES UP, AND CHARRED AND RAGGED SKIN IS EBONY FEATHERS AGAIN, AND HE'S IN HIS CAVE WITH EVE.

EVE. WOMAN ONCE HIS WIFE AND NOW HIS COMPANION IN NIGHTMARES. MOTHER OF REGRET. MOTHER OF THE WORLD.

YOU WERE DREAMING, MATTHEW.

IN *HER* CAVE, THE SAFE SMELL OF DUST AND SHADOWS ABOUT HIM.

YEAH.

I DIDN'T SAY ANYTHING STUPID THIS TIME, DID I?

NO. YOU DIDN'T SAY ANYTHING AT ALL.

GOOD.

...AND WHEN HE WAKES UP, HE'S STILL IN THE ROTTING OLD HOUSE ON ST. CHARLES, AND HE'S STILL ALONE.

IN THE DREAM, ECHO STILL HAS BOTH HIS EYES. AND HE STILL HAS GABRIEL.

IN THE DREAM, HE HAS FEELINGS BESIDES ANGER AND THE QUIET AND SEETHING RAGE. BESIDES LONELINESS.

HE SLEEPS A LOT THESE DAYS.

WHEN HE'S AWAKE, HE RARELY LEAVES THE HOUSE. KEEPS THESE MOLDROTTEN BOARDS ABOUT HIM LIKE A CARAPACE OR WINDING SHROUD.

THE FUCKING HOUSE, A PLACE HE CAN STAY, PLACE TO SLEEP, SAGGING ROOF OVER HIS HEAD.

RENT-FREE AS LONG AS HE COMES WHEN THE OLD QUEEN FROM THE QUARTER CALLS, AS LONG AS HE BENDS OVER WHEN HE'S TOLD.

THE OLD QUEEN MAKES HIM TAKE THE PATCH OFF. HITS HIM NOW AND THEN. BUT NEVER HARD ENOUGH TO LEAVE A MARK.

IT COULD BE WORSE. IT COULD ALMOST ALWAYS BE WORSE.

AND IT BUYS HIM TIME.

THE DOORKNOB LIKE ICE IN HIS HAND AND IT ALWAYS SURPRISES HIM, THE COLD SPOT AT THE THRESHOLD. HE SHOULD BE USED TO IT BY NOW.

THE WAY HE SHOULD BE USED TO THE SOUNDS IT MAKES. RAGGED SOUNDS LIKE TEARING CLOTH AND SOMEONE CRYING IN A DARK PLACE.

SOUND LIKE WAITING, AND WANTING, AND LOSS.

AND THE CHRISTMAS SMELL OF ORANGES.

WHY DON'T YOU OPEN THE DOOR, IT SAYS, WHISPERS, AND THAT'S THE WORST.

HORNET VOICES. LOCUST SIGHS.

"I'M SORRY," HE SAYS AND HEARS THE THING IT DOES INSTEAD OF SMILING.

AND OPEN THE DOOR, ECHO, IT SAYS.

JULY AND THE BRASS IS COLD AS FUCKING ICE.

OPEN THE DOOR.

TODAY, IT SAYS. *THIS IS THE DAY,* AND ECHO FEELS THE WORLD SLIPPING OUT FROM UNDER HIM, WORDS HE'S LIVED FOR AND NEVER REALLY THOUGHT HE'D HEAR.

NOT SURE NOW HE EVER *WANTED* TO HEAR THEM.

ROLLER COASTER STOMACH DROP, COLD PLUNGE, COLDER SWEAT, BUT ALREADY REACHING FOR THAT SMALL, CALM PLACE HE'S KEPT SAFE FOR THIS MOMENT.

GOOD. IT'S ABOUT TIME.

ABOUT TIME. YES, SWEET ECHO. IT'S *ALL* ABOUT TIME, ISN'T IT?

I'M NOT IN THE MOOD FOR YOUR FUCKING RIDDLES TODAY, ARCANE.

YOU'RE *CERTAIN* THAT IT'S TIME?

I HAVE IT ON THE BEST AUTHORITY. SUNSPOTS. MARS AND JUPITER. IF THIS IS WHAT YOU WANT... IF THIS IS REALLY WHAT YOU WANT, SWEET, SWEET ECHO.

YOU *KNOW* IT'S WHAT I WANT.

THEN TALK WITH THE PLACES *BETWEEN* THE STARS. REACH OUT TO THE ONE THAT GOES BY *CORINTHIAN...*

SO, ANYHOW, ABUDAH WOUND UP TRYING TO DUMP THE WHOLE DAMN BUCKET DOWN THE DRAIN BEFORE MERV COULD STOP HIM.

HALF THE PLUMBING IN THE PALACE IS CLOGGED WITH THE THINGS AND MERV'S PANTIES ARE REALLY IN A WAD OVER IT.

THAT'S AWFUL, MATTHEW.

WELL, YEAH, BUT IT'S PRETTY GODDAMN FUNNY, TOO.

YES, I GUESS IT IS.

YEP, OL' ABUDAH REALLY SCREWED THE POOCH THIS TIME. I DON'T EVEN KNOW WHERE THEY FOUND THAT MANY DAMN HAIR-BALLS IN THE FIRST PLACE...

HEY! WHOA. WHAT THE HELL WAS THAT?

WHAT? IS SOMETHING WRONG?

UH, SHIT. I DON'T KNOW.

SORTA LIKE A POSSUM ON MY GRAVE, YOU KNOW? 'CEPT MORE LIKE A *HERD* OF POSSUMS.

BRRRRR. *JESUS*, IT'S *COLD* IN HERE.

IT ISN'T COLD, MATTHEW...

WELL, I'M *FREEZING*.

IT'S LIKE THE *BOSS* IS CALLING ME, OR *LUCIEN*, BUT IT AIN'T *NEITHER* OF THEM. IT'S... CAN'T YOU *FEEL* IT?

MATTHEW!

WHAT...?

JESUS!

SQUAWK!

ALL OF THIS IS TOO SUDDEN TO MAKE SENSE, AND EVE IS WATCHING FROM SOMEWHERE OUTSIDE HERSELF.

LET GO OF ME, YOU SONOFA... ≋SQUAWK!≋

AND THAT'S GOOD, SHE THINKS, BECAUSE IT KEEPS THE FEAR FROM GETTING IN HER WAY.

EVE! GET OUTTA HERE!

NO, MATTHEW. I'M NOT LEAVING YOU. I WON'T JUST LET IT TAKE YOU...

AND IT STOPS HER FROM ACTING ON ANYTHING BUT INSTINCT.

AND THEN IT'S GONE, THE EBONY HORROR THAT STANK OF DUST AND VENGEANCE AND CITRUS, AND SHE FALLS HARD BACK INTO HERSELF, AND THERE'S NOTHING TO SHIELD HER FROM THE KNOWLEDGE THAT IT'S TAKEN HIM.

THE KNOWLEDGE THAT SHE'S ALONE.

TURN HIM LOOSE!

ALMOST ENOUGH DISTANCE FROM HERSELF TO BLOCK THE SUDDEN PAIN, SEARING ACID COLD PAST COLD AND THE BLACKNESS IS LIKE TOUCHING EVERY FILTHY THING SHE'S EVER SEEN OR IMAGINED.

NO! MATTHEW!

MATTHEW. OH GOD...

IT'S OVER, ALMOST BEFORE IT BEGAN, AND HE'S AFRAID TO LOOK, AFRAID TO SEE.

EVERYTHING THE SPIRIT CALLED ARCANE HAS TAUGHT HIM AND PARTS OF HIMSELF HE COULDN'T SPARE GONE IN THE SUMMONING AND HE ACHES LIKE TETANUS AND STRYCHNINE.

UNNHHHH... IT SIGHS BEHIND HIM, TAKES UP ALL THAT'S LEFT OF THE WORLD BACK THERE, AND ECHO FEELS ITS CONFUSION BEFORE HE OPENS HIS EYES, RAGE SWELLING LIKE AN ANGRY, VIOLATED HIVE.

IT'S NO SURPRISE, THOUGH. SICK, INEVITABLE DISAPPOINTMENT, BUT NO SURPRISE THAT THE CREATURE THAT STALKED HIM AND GABRIEL FROM SHERMAN'S MARCH TO NEW ORLEANS ISN'T COWERING, HELPLESS BEFORE HIM.

BEHIND ECHO, THE BUZZ RISES, JUMPING ANGRY OCTAVES, TO BECOME A WHIRRING STORM OF WINGS AND BARBS.

YOU'RE REALLY NOT VERY GOOD AT THIS SORT OF THING, ARE YOU, DEAR? HE THINKS AND HEARS HIMSELF LAUGHING THROUGH THE GATHERING INSECT WAIL.

YOU'VE FAILED ME, IT GROWLS, STICKY WORDS COUGHED FROM A HONEYCOMB, ANTHILL THROAT.

YOU'VE FAILED...

NOPE. NOT MUCH OF A WITCH AT ALL. BUT IT DOESN'T MATTER.

...UNFIT FOR A CONDUIT, UNCLEAN LITTLE FAGGOT.

UNCLEAN, UNWORTHY LITTLE FAG.

IF HE'S FAILED, AT LEAST HE'S TRIED.

YOU KNOW, YOU TALK REAL BIG FOR SOMETHING THAT HAS TO HIDE UNDER A PILE OF BUGS.

PISS OFF, FUCKER.

AND FRANKLY, HE JUST DOESN'T GIVE A SHIT ANYMORE.

I SHOULD KILL YOU NOW.

THEN DO IT AND SHUT THE HELL UP.

NO!

YOU HAVEN'T EARNED THE MERCY...

HE'S ONLY HEARD THIS SOUND ONCE BEFORE. EIGHT YEARS OLD AND A TORNADO PASSING LOW OVERHEAD, HUDDLED BENEATH A MATTRESS WITH HIS MOTHER AND LITTLE SISTER AS A RABID GEORGIA SKY HOWLED AND RAGED.

THIS IS NOT *EXACTLY* THE SAME SOUND, BUT IT'S CLOSE, CLOSE ENOUGH.

HIS SKIN ON FIRE, AND SO MAYBE IT'LL KILL HIM AFTER ALL, HE THINKS A LITTLE HOPEFULLY, JUST BEFORE IT REACHES OUT AND TOUCHES HIS MIND. FONDLES HIS SOUL.

AND SHOWS HIM THE TRUTH, THAT THIS SPELL WAS NEVER MEANT FOR THE CORINTHIAN.

COULD YOU REALLY BELIEVE THAT *YOU* HELD ME?

YES. OF COURSE YOU COULD. OF COURSE YOU DID.

EVEN AFTER WHAT YOUR POOR BLIND BOY DID TO YOU, EVEN AFTER HE TOOK YOUR EYE AND LEFT YOU CRAWLING IN BLOOD AND SHIT, YOU THOUGHT THERE WAS *POWER* FOR *YOU*.

THAT'S ALWAYS THE WAY OF *PAWNS*, ISN'T IT?

DEAR, SWEET, UNWITTING ECHO,

YOU CAN'T EVEN BEGIN TO *IMAGINE* VENGEANCE.

I'D TAKE YOU WITH ME, JUST FOR *KICKS*, BUT YOU HAVEN'T EVEN EARNED MY *COMPANY*.

THE FEEL OF IT AGAINST HIS SKIN, THE ANGRYSLICK TOUCH OF IT IN HIS HEAD, ANOTHER SECOND OF THAT AND HE WOULD HAVE BEEN COMPLETELY AND GRATEFULLY INSANE.

SO IT WITHDRAWS.

AND LEAVES TWO NAMES IN HIS HEAD AS IT GOES --*MATTHEW* AND *MATT CABLE*-- AND IT LAUGHS AT HIM, THEN.

THERE'S THE SOUND OF GLASS BREAKING...

AND HE'S STILL ALIVE.

STILL ALIVE, THE RAVEN THINKS, AND THE THOUGHT SEEMS VERY LOUD.

"*EVE?*" HE WHISPERS, THE NOTHING ABOUT HIM SO PROFOUND HE'S AFRAID OF DISTURBING IT. BUT THERE'S NO ANSWER.

NOWHERE, FOR A STAGNANT SPACE OF TIME THAT HE CAN'T COUNT. A VERY LONG INSTANT OR VERY SHORT CENTURY, SOMETHING INDEFINITE THAT ISN'T EITHER. INDEFINITE AS THE CHILLING NOTHING...

WHEN HE FLAPS HIS WINGS THERE'S NO RESISTANCE, AND WHEN HE SCRATCHES WITH HIS FEET, NO GROUND. BUT NO SENSE THAT HE'S FALLING. NO SENSE AT ALL.

BUT HE ISN'T DEAD. BEEN THERE, *TWICE*. DONE THAT, BOUGHT THE DAMNED T-SHIRT, AND IT WASN'T ANYTHING LIKE *THIS*, EITHER TIME. SO AT LEAST HE ISN'T DEAD.

AT LEAST, HE *THINKS* HE ISN'T DEAD.

AND THEN THE SOFT SIZZLE OF RAIN AND THE GHOST OF THE MEMORY OF A FAMILIAR VOICE, FAMILIAR VOICES...

...UNWORTHY LITTLE FAG.

YOU KNOW, YOU TALK REAL BIG...

THE RAIN IS EASIER TO LISTEN TO, EASIER TO FOLLOW.

THE SKY FALLING, GENTLE AND *COOL*, AND AT LEAST THAT MEANS THERE *IS* A SKY.

AND IF THERE'S A SKY, THEN THERE'S AN EARTH.

AND A PLACE FOR HIM, SOMEWHERE BETWEEN THE TWO.

HE HASN'T FELT HALF THIS SHITTY IN A VERY LONG TIME.

COLD AND WET AND PAIN EVERYWHERE, PAIN AND NAUSEA AND HIS HEAD LIKE A BAD TOOTH.

JESUS, I DON'T WANNA FUCKIN' PUKE, HE THINKS, HAS ALWAYS HATED PUKING.

AND THEN HE SEES HIS *HANDS.*

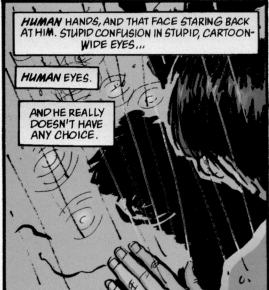

HUMAN HANDS, AND THAT FACE STARING BACK AT HIM. STUPID CONFUSION IN STUPID, CARTOON-WIDE EYES...

HUMAN EYES.

AND HE REALLY DOESN'T HAVE ANY CHOICE.

THERE GO THE TWO FIELD MICE HE PATIENTLY LET RIPEN FOR DAYS, STASHED AT THE BACK OF THE CAVE.

WHAT A WASTE, AND THAT ALMOST MAKES HIM LAUGH.

HOW LONG SINCE HE'S *LAUGHED*?

RAVENS DON'T LAUGH. IT'S NOT THAT THEY DON'T HAVE A SENSE OF HUMOR ...

...BUT THEY DON'T *LAUGH*.

HE FEELS THE PRICKLY LITTLE HAIRS ON THE BACK OF HIS HAND, SCRUBBING ROUGH ACROSS FLESHY LIPS, LIPS PRESSED AGAINST FIRM HUMAN TEETH.

JESUS.

JESUS CHRIST. HE'S A MAN AGAIN.

THE STUBBLE ON HIS CHEEK, THE MINUTE WHORLS OF HIS FINGERPRINTS.

NO WAY, MAN. NO FUCKING WAY. AND EVEN HIS *MIND* IS A MAN'S MIND.

LIKE ARISTEAS, HE THINKS, SOLID UNDENIABLE MAN THOUGHTS, AND HIS EYES ARE BURNING AND IT TAKES A SECOND TO REMEMBER WHAT THAT MEANS.

THAT HE'S *CRYING*.

145

CRYING.

HEY, YOU GOTTA LOOK AT THIS!

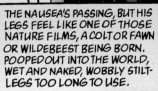

THE NAUSEA'S PASSING, BUT HIS LEGS FEEL LIKE ONE OF THOSE NATURE FILMS, A COLT OR FAWN OR WILDEBEEST BEING BORN, POOPED OUT INTO THE WORLD, WET AND NAKED, WOBBLY STILT-LEGS TOO LONG TO USE.

NO, MAN. IT'S SOME BUCK-NAKED *WHITE* DUDE!

ALIEN MUSCLES, MYSTERY EXERTIONS. OUT OF HIS ELEMENT.

AND HE CAN'T STOP CRYING.

NO, MAN. I DON'T *KNOW.* HE'S JUST *STANDIN'* THERE!

OH, MAN...

WHAT YOU THINK YOU *DOIN',* CRACKHEAD?

WHAT'S *THIS* HAPPY BULLSHIT?

KINDA LATE FOR MARDI GRAS...

OKAY, FOLKS. SHOW'S OVER.

C'MON, BUDDY...

POLICE

HERE, HALF AN HOUR NOW SINCE IT LEFT AND ECHO'S STILL SITTING HERE, WATCHING THE PRETTY BLACK ROCK. TRYING NOT TO WONDER WHAT COMES NEXT.

TRYING NOT TO THINK. NOT TO HEAR ITS VOICE (...*UNCLEAN, UNWORTHY...*). BETTER JUST TO WATCH THE PRETTY BLACK ROCK.

MAYBE IT'S WORTH A LOT OF MONEY.

MAYBE ENOUGH FOR BUS FARE OUT OF THIS STINKING SHITHOLE OF A CITY.

THEN AGAIN, MAYBE IT'S WORTH A LOT MORE THAN THAT.

AND *HERE*, SHE ISN'T SURE HOW LONG SINCE THE OILY, LIVING DARK SLIPPED INSIDE HER SANCTUARY AND DRAGGED THE RAVEN AWAY.

KEEP BUSY, KEEP MOVING, AND SO THERE'S ANOTHER BIT OF HIM SAFE, COLLECTED.

A LONG TIME SINCE SHE'S NOTICED HIS LITTLE MESSES. A LONGER TIME SINCE IT'S MATTERED.

WE'RE GONNA NEED MORE THAN THAT, SHE THINKS AND REMEMBERS AN OLD HEDGEHOG PUT AWAY FOR ST. CRISPIN'S DAY. AND EVE GOES BACK TO WORK.

HOUMA, LOUISIANA:

THE SHITTY LITTLE APARTMENT IS VERY HOT AND SHE'S TALKING WITH A DETECTIVE FROM NEW ORLEANS.

THERE *HAS* TO BE A MISTAKE, OFFICER.

MY HUSBAND... MY *EX*-HUSBAND IS DEAD.

SO HOT SHE COULD BE BACK IN SOUTH AMERICA. THE DETECTIVE'S QUESTIONS ARE AS SENSELESS AS THE HEAT, THE CLINGING AIR LIKE STAGNANT, DIRTY WATER.

HE'S BEEN DEAD FOR A LONG TIME. WHAT? OH, UM, EIGHTY-NINE. MAY, EIGHTY-NINE.

HE ISN'T LISTENING.

YES, I'M *SURE*. JESUS CHRIST.

YES, OF COURSE I UNDERSTAND THAT YOU HAVE TO BE SURE, BUT...

NO, I *DON'T* WANT TO TALK TO HIM. WAIT, PLEASE...

BUT IT'S TOO LATE AND THERE'S THE SILENCE AS THE PHONE AT THE OTHER END OF THE CON-NECTION CHANGES HANDS.

AND THEN HIS VOICE.

HIS VOICE.

ABBY? ABBY, ARE YOU *THERE*? AND IT'S IMPOSSIBLE AND THERE'S ABSOLUTELY NO DOUBT IN HER MIND THAT IT'S HIM.

ABBY? CAN YOU HEAR ME? HE SOUNDS SO FUCKING *LOST*. HE WAS ALWAYS SO *GOOD* AT SOUNDING LOST.

NO...

NO.

THE APARTMENT IS VERY HOT.

149

SHE WAITS AND AT LEAST IT DOESN'T RING AGAIN.

THERE'S ONLY THE HEAT AND THE SWEAT AND THE SOUND OF TRAFFIC OUT ON THE STREETS OF HOUMA. THE IMPATIENT SOUND OF A FLY AT THE WINDOW SCREEN.

THERE'S NO WAY IT COULD HAVE BEEN MATT. MATT'S DEAD AND IN HIS GRAVE.

DEAD TEN YEARS NOW, ALMOST.

MORE CRAZY BULLSHIT IN THOSE TEN YEARS THAN ANYONE DESERVES IN A LIFETIME --

--ENOUGH FOR A *HUNDRED* LIFETIMES.

ENOUGH *LOSS* AND ENOUGH *REUNION*. ENOUGH *TRICKS*.

ENOUGH.

IT *WASN'T* HIM. IT COULD NOT HAVE *BEEN* HIM.

NOT IN A SANE WORLD.

AND ALL SHE'S ASKING OF THE WORLD THESE DAYS IS A LITTLE SANITY.

JESUS, IT'S *SO* HOT.

SO. WHAT'S THE STORY, BUBBA?

SHE HUNG UP ON ME.

YEAH? WELL, I REALLY DON'T THINK THE LADY KNOWS YOU FROM ADAM, BUBBA.

SHE SAID HER HUSBAND'S DEAD.

YEAH... I AM.

KNOWS YOU FROM ADAM.

YEAH? ALL RIGHT, BUBBA, YOU JUST SIT STILL FOR ME. WE'RE GONNA NEED TO HAVE A TALK WITH A DOCTOR...

KNOWS YOU FROM EVE...

HEY, I SAID SIT STILL!

HE'S DEAD, AND GOD, THE WORLD IS HEAVY.

LOOK, I DON'T WANNA HAVE TO PUT THE CUFFS BACK ON YOU. JESUS, FRANKIE, HELP ME WITH THIS GUY.

THE WORLD IS HEAVY.

AND HE CAN'T REMEMBER HOW TO FLY AWAY.

END OF PART ONE

IT'S NEVER BEEN AN *EASY* JOB, BEING THE LIBRARIAN OF DREAMS, SOLE CURATOR OF UNFULFILLED PHANTASMS, SHEPHERD OF MISPLACED AND MISCREANT SHADOWS AND ROMANCE.

HE'S NEVER *ASKED* THAT IT BE EASY.

IT WAS HIS *REWARD*, AFTER ALL. HIS REWARD FOR DUTIES RENDERED IN THE SERVICE OF HIS LORD, AN *AGE* OF SERVICE.

AND REWARDS ARE, OFTEN AS NOT, A MATTER OF RESPONSIBILITY.

ON THE STAIRS TO THE CONSERVATORY, THE FASHION THING IS MAKING A FUSS BECAUSE ITS NEW BURGUNDY VELVET DOC MARTEN WORK BOOTS ARE WET, AND THE ERMINE CUFFS OF ITS BELLBOTTOMS.

AND SOMETIMES, WELL, LUCIEN MISSES THE OLD DAYS.

HE ASKS THE INTERRUPTED SUICIDE IF HE'S SEEN MATTHEW, AND HE SHOULD HAVE KNOWN BETTER. THE BOY ONLY MUMBLES SOMETHING ABOUT DROWNING AND STARTS TO CRY.

SORRY TO DISTURB YOU, THEN.

NOT THIS EVENING, LIBRARIAN. HAVE YOU CHECKED EVE'S CAVE? HE'S SPENDING A LOT OF TIME WITH EVE THESE DAYS.

STILL A LITTLE SHAKEN UP BY THAT BUSINESS WITH THE TRICKSTER, I THINK.

YOU'VE HEARD ABOUT THAT?

WE HEAR EVERYTHING, LIBRARIAN. SOONER OR LATER, WE HEAR IT ALL.

TOO BUSY WITH THE SOPPY MESS IN THE LIBRARY TO BE WORRIED UNTIL NOW, THAT MATTHEW DIDN'T COME WHEN HE CALLED. AND NOW, THERE'S NO SENSE OF HIM ANYWHERE IN THE DREAMING.

NO SENSE OF HIM AT ALL.

A SHORTCUT INTO NIGHTMARE, PUSHING DOWN HIS APPREHENSION. *ENOUGH* TO WORRY ABOUT ALREADY, WITH THE PALACE PASSING FOR *ATLANTIS* OR *R'LYEH* AND HIS BOOKS LIKE SPONGES.

SOMETIMES IT'S HARD *NOT* TO MISS THE OLD DAYS.

AFTER HIS UNREMARKABLE DEATH, DYING IN HIS SLEEP ON THE SANDY-WARM SHORES OF THE EUPHRATES, EASY DEATH AFTER A LONG LIFE AND DYING HADN'T BEEN SO BAD.

A LOT OF *STORIES* STILL UNTOLD, OF COURSE, BUT A STRONG DAUGHTER LEFT TO TELL THEM.

"WOULD YOU BE MY RAVEN, SON OF ADAM? I HAVE NEED OF A RAVEN."

AND HE SAID YES, JUST A DREAM, HE THOUGHT, SO HE SAID YES BECAUSE IT SEEMED BETTER THAN THE BOREDOM OF BEING DEAD.

ALL THOSE MILLENNIA AGO. AND EVEN *THEN*, SO CLOSE TO THE START, MEN HAD LACKED THE GOOD SENSE NOT TO PLACE THE WORD *"JUST"* BEFORE *"DREAM."*

IN ÆTERNUM!

EVE? MATTHEW?

AND THEN HE HEARS HER, CRYING. THE LONELIEST SOUND. AND THE LIBRARIAN OF DREAMS FORGETS EVERYTHING ELSE.

WHAT'S HAPPENED, EVE? WHERE'S MATTHEW?

HE'S *GONE*. IT CAME AND TOOK HIM AWAY AND THERE WAS *NOTHING* I COULD DO TO STOP IT.

NOTHING, LUCIEN, NOTHING AT ALL.

YOUR HAND...

IT CAME INTO *MY* CAVE AND *TOOK* HIM, AND THERE WAS NOTHING I COULD DO TO STOP IT.

I DON'T UNDERSTAND. *WHAT* TOOK HIM?

I DON'T KNOW *WHAT* IT WAS. I DON'T *CARE* WHAT IT WAS. IT TOOK HIM AND I COULDN'T STOP IT, LUCIEN.

I CAN'T FEEL HIM. I CAN'T FEEL HIM ANYWHERE AT ALL.

WE'LL HAVE TO GO BACK TO THE PALACE, THEN. IF ANYONE SHOULD KNOW WHERE MATTHEW'S BEEN TAKEN, IF ANYONE CAN FIND HIM...

NO! THIS ISN'T HIS FIGHT, LUCIEN. NOT THIS TIME...

MATTHEW IS *HIS* RAVEN, EVE?

NO. MATTHEW IS HIS *OWN* RAVEN, AND I'M NOT HELPLESS...

HE'S GONE AGAIN. HE'S JUST *GONE.*

YES, I KNOW. BUT WE'LL FIND HIM, IF THAT'S HOW YOU THINK WE SHOULD PROCEED.

IT'S... I'M SO EMPTY WITHOUT HIM, LUCIEN.

THEN I'LL BE YOUR RAVEN AGAIN, UNTIL WE FIND HIM.

I *THINK* I REMEMBER HOW.

LUCIEN...

I IMAGINE IT'S NOT UNLIKE SWIMMING, OR LEARNING TO RIDE A UNICYCLE, OR HOPSCOTCH.

LUCIEN, IT'S NOT NECESSARY. I CAN'T ASK THAT OF YOU.

YOU *DIDN'T* ASK, EVE. YOU DON'T HAVE TO ASK.

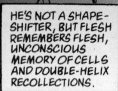

HE'S NOT A SHAPE-SHIFTER, BUT FLESH REMEMBERS FLESH, UNCONSCIOUS MEMORY OF CELLS AND DOUBLE-HELIX RECOLLECTIONS.

BONE REMEMBERS BONE, EVEN IF THE MEMORIES ARE FADED YELLOW THINGS, BRITTLE AT THE EDGES.

AND IT WASN'T HIS DOING THE FIRST TIME AROUND, SO HE'S HAVING TO WORK FROM HOW IT *FELT*, HIS MEMORY OF HOW IT FELT, TRANSFORMATION FROM THE GHOST OF A MAN TO THE DREAM OF A BIRD.

WORKING BACK, REVERSING STEPS, DREAM OF A MAN INTO THE DIMLY RECALLED DREAM OF A BIRD.

HE WISHES HE'D PAID BETTER ATTENTION...

HE KNOWS MORE OF ANATOMY AND EVOLUTION THAN MAGIC AND SO IT'S SLOW AND CLUMSY. AND IT *HURTS.*

FUSION OF CARPALS AND TARSALS, FEATHERS FROM HIS SKIN LIKE RAZOR QUILLS.

AND HE CAN'T HELP FEELING EMBARRASSED. AWKWARD. WISHES HE'D STEPPED OUTSIDE SO SHE WOULDN'T HAVE TO SEE.

UNNNH...

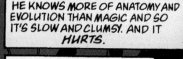

STERNUM TO WISHBONE, CHEST STRONG FOR BEATING WINGS, SHARP CLAWS FOR TEARING DEAD FLESH.

THE GREENSTICK POP OF HIS SKULL, BRAIN ON FIRE; NEW EYES, TEETH AND JAWS TRADED FOR THIS FINE SHARP BEAK.

OH, LUCIEN...

AND IT'S DONE.

TEN THOUSAND YEARS SINCE HE'S WORN THIS SKIN, MORE OR LESS...

...AND LUCIEN ALMOST FORGETS THE URGENCY, *WHY* HE'S DONE THIS, IN THE RUSH OF RAVEN-THOUGHTS AND RAVENBLOOD THROUGH HIS VEINS.

AND THEN SHE'S TOUCHING HIM, LIFTS HIM, AND HER TOUCH...

HER TOUCH BRINGS HIM BACK.

NEW ORLEANS, CHARITY HOSPITAL.

TWO DAYS SINCE THE CALL. SHE ISN'T *SUP-POSED* TO BE HERE, THIS WHITE, WHITE ROOM THAT STINKS OF DISINFECTANT AND INSANITY.

"JUST A MINUTE, MS. ARCANE," THE NURSE SAID AND NOW SHE'S BEEN SITTING HERE OVER HALF AN HOUR.

WAITING.

WHY, SHE THINKS AGAIN, THE WORD THROUGH HER HEAD LIKE COUNTING BEADS, *WHY THE FUCK AM I DOING THIS?*

WHY THE FUCK...

SHE STILL DOESN'T HAVE AN ANSWER FOR HERSELF. NOTHING GOOD ENOUGH, ANYWAY. NOTHING THAT MAKES ENOUGH SENSE.

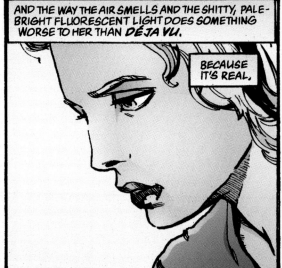

AND THE WAY THE AIR SMELLS AND THE SHITTY, PALE-BRIGHT FLUORESCENT LIGHT DOES SOMETHING WORSE TO HER THAN *DÉJA VU.*

BECAUSE IT'S REAL.

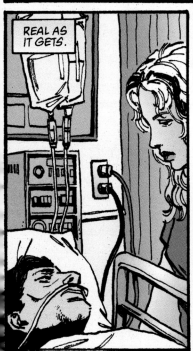

REAL AS IT GETS.

FUCK.

MS. ARCANE? YOU MAY SEE HIM NOW.

UM, YEAH... THANKS.

IT SHOULD BE *SIMPLE*, TRACING THE DISTANCE BETWEEN THESE RAGGED BITS OF MATTHEW AND THE PLACE OR TIME HE'S BEEN TAKEN.

ASTROLOGERS' STRAIGHT LINES BETWEEN STARS FOR CONSTELLATION ANIMALS, ARCHITECTS' LINES, LONGITUDE, LATITUDE.

RIGHT ANGLES. ACUTE INTERSECTIONS.

DOT-TO-DOT.

IT SHOULD BE SIMPLE.

MATTHEW...?

AND THEN SHE FEELS HIM, FAINT, AND WRONG, AND FAR AWAY.

BUT ENOUGH OF HIM TO HOLD ONTO.

HE'S VERY SICK, LUCIEN, OR DYING.

ENOUGH TO PULL THEM THROUGH.

CHARITY HOSPITAL.

THEY SAID SHE'S *HERE*, THAT SHE CAME, AND HE WANTS TO THINK CLEARLY.

BUT THE PILLS THEY GIVE HIM HAVE TURNED THE WORLD SOFT AND UNCERTAIN, AND HE'S NOT EVEN SURE THIS ISN'T A *DREAM*.

SHIT. IT COULD ALL BE A DREAM.

THE THINGS HE'S BEEN TELLING THE SHRINKS: MY NAME IS MATT JOHN CABLE.

EVERYTHING SEEMS AS REAL AS ANYTHING ELSE, OR AS UNREAL.

AND THEY GIVE HIM THESE LITTLE RED PILLS WHEN HE WAKES UP AT NIGHT, SCREAM-ING.

I USED TO BE A SECRET AGENT.

I USED TO BE A FUCKING BIG BLACK BIRD. I LIVED IN A CAVE FULL OF NIGHTMARES WITH A WOMAN NAMED EVE.

YEAH. *THAT* EVE.

SCREAMING *HER* NAME.

BECAUSE THEY ASK, HE TELLS THEM HOW COLD HELL IS, AND HOW AN INCH MIGHT AS WELL BE A MILLION FUCKING MILES.

THE PAIN AND CONFUSION AND DESPAIR IN HER SOUL'S FACE, LOOKING UP AT HIM FROM HER DAMNATION.

THEY DON'T LIKE IT WHEN HE TALKS ABOUT *FLYING*. IT MAKES THEM VERY NERVOUS.

MATT...? OH GOD, MATT.

THIS BOX BENEATH HEAVEN.

UT THEY SMILE, ND NOD THEIR EADS, AND IVE HIM MORE PILLS.

"IT'S A MEMORY KIND OF SKY..." JESUS. WHAT'S THAT? SOMETHING HE HEARD ONCE, A BIT OF SONG, MAYBE, AND HE FEELS SO SMALL IN THIS BOX.

HOW?

YOU CUT YOUR HAIR.

JESUS, MATT. I WATCHED YOU DIE...

IT LOOKS NICE, ABBY, IT LOOKS REAL NICE THAT WAY.

MATT, WILL YOU SHUT UP ABOUT MY GODDAMN HAIR? GOOD GOD...

I'M SORRY. IT WAS JUST A SHOCK, THAT'S ALL.

OH, THAT'S FUNNY. I CAN'T BELIEVE YOU SAID THAT.

I DON'T THINK I BELIEVE ANY OF THIS.

I COULD TRY AND EXPLAIN, BUT I THINK IT'D ONLY MAKE THINGS WORSE. YOU'D NEVER BUY MOST OF IT.

DON'T COUNT ON IT. I'VE BEEN THROUGH SOME PRETTY WEIRD SHIT SINCE YOU, UM...SINCE YOU DIED.

YEAH. ME TOO, I GUESS.

JESUS, MATT.

SHE HADN'T EXPECTED THE WAKING WORLD. SHOULD HAVE EXPECTED ANYTHING, ANY-WHERE, AND HER HEAD FEELS TOO LIGHT, HER BELLY TOO HEAVY.

ARE YOU BEGINNING TO FEEL BETTER?

MMMHM. A LITTLE, MAYBE. IT'S BEEN A VERY LONG TIME...

LONGER THAN SHE CAN REMEM-BER, REALLY, SINCE SHE WAS AMONG THE WAKING...

...SO MANY MILLENNIA SPENT IN DREAMS, IN THE VELVET FOLDS OF NIGHTMARE THOUGHTS.

THE WHITE NOISE STATIC OF SO MANY HUMAN MINDS WIDE AWAKE, LIKE FINGER-NAILS ON SLATE AND IT MAKES HER TEETH HURT AND A DULL PAIN AT THE BACKS OF HER EYES.

WHERE THE HELL ARE WE, LUCIEN?

NEW ORLEANS, LOUISIANA. IN AMERICA. THE VIEUX CARRÉ, I SUSPECT, TO BE PRECISE.

MOMMA, THAT BIRD WAS SAYING SOMETHING!

SHE'S A VENTRILOQUIST, HONEY. SHE ONLY MADE IT SOUND LIKE THE BIRD WAS TALKING.

YOU'RE REALLY VERY GOOD. THAT MUST HAVE TAKEN A LOT OF PRACTICE TO LEARN.

YES... THANK YOU.

MAYBE YOU SHOULDN'T TALK QUITE SO LOUD, LUCIEN.

POINT TAKEN.

AMERICA. SHE'S NEVER BEEN IN AMERICA. SHE WOULD RATHER NOT BE HERE NOW.

CAN YOU FEEL HIM?

NO, I CAN'T. I CAN'T FEEL HIM AT ALL.

NEITHER CAN I.

I CAN'T EVEN *THINK* HERE. WE HAVE TO FIND SOMEPLACE *QUIET,* SOMEPLACE THERE AREN'T SO MANY PEOPLE...

THERE WERE NEVER SO MANY OF THEM, BEFORE. A LITTLE BEHIND THE TIMES, EVE, DEAR, AND YEAH, AGREEING WITH HERSELF. AND *I* LIKE IT THAT WAY.

I'LL HAVE A LOOK AROUND, THEN, IF YOU'LL BE ALL RIGHT ALONE FOR A LITTLE WHILE?

YES. PLEASE. *ANYTHING.* A PARK, A GRAVEYARD, THE CITY *DUMP* WOULD DO...

SO HE GOES, RISES AS EAGER FOR THE AIR AS HE IS RELUCTANT TO LEAVE HER BEHIND.

THE BLUE WELCOME OF THE SKY, AND DUTY, AND HIM CAUGHT SOMEWHERE IN THE MIDDLE.

THE SLIPSTREAM AIR ACROSS HIS FEATHERS, SMALL HEART POUNDING FRANTIC AGAINST THE ANVIL OF RED MUSCLE AND WHITE BREASTBONE; IT WOULD BE SO EASY TO *FORGET* HIM-SELF IN THIS...

UPSTROKE, DOWNSTROKE, THE TIN WHISTLE ROAR OF THE WIND AND THE LIBRARIAN CAN'T RE-MEMBER THE LAST TIME HE FELT HALF THIS *ALIVE.*

HALF THIS *FREE.*

CHARITY HOSPITAL

IT'S NOT THAT SIMPLE, MATT.

FOR FUCK'S SAKE, ABBY. GIVE ME A **CHANCE**...

MATT... PLEASE.

WE COULD AT LEAST **TRY**, COULDN'T WE?

AND THERE IT IS, SHE'S SAID IT. **NO.** SO NONE OF THIS MEANS A GODDAMN THING.

NO, I DON'T THINK SO.

PURGATORY ALL FOR NOTHING, AND WAY DOWN INSIDE HE FEELS SOMETHING START TO STIR, SOMETHING **BAD** HE HASN'T FELT FOR A VERY LONG TIME.

IT TASTES LIKE BILE AND REGRET, A LITTLE LIKE ORANGES, AT THE BACK OF HIS THROAT. ORANGES, COMING BACK UP.

HE TRIES TO IGNORE IT.

YOU AT LEAST OWE ME THE CHANCE TO SHOW YOU.

BUT IT DOESN'T WANT TO BE IGNORED.

YOU JUST SLOW DOWN A GODDAMN SECOND, MATT!

DO YOU HAVE ANY *IDEA* WHAT YOU'RE ASKING? DO YOU HAVE THE SLIGHTEST FUCKING IDEA? YOU DON'T EVEN KNOW WHO I *AM*, WHO I'VE *BECOME!*

SO YOU'RE JUST GONNA HAVE TO BACK OFF, OKAY?

SINCE YOU'VE BEEN GONE, I'VE HAD *ANOTHER* HUSBAND AND I'VE HAD A *BABY*, MATT, AND THAT DOESN'T EVEN START TO SCRATCH THE *SURFACE* OF ALL THE WEIRD SHIT THAT'S HAPPENED TO ME.

SINCE YOU'VE BEEN *DEAD*, MATT.

YOU'VE BEEN GONE *TWELVE* YEARS...

AND I'M SORRY AS HELL, BUT I DON'T *OWE* YOU SHIT.

IT DOESN'T WANT TO BE IGNORED AT ALL. BUT HE PUSHES AT IT, SHOVES IT BACK INSIDE....

BECAUSE *HE* ISN'T THE SAME PERSON, EITHER. HE'S HARDLY TOLD HER ANYTHING, THE THINGS HE'S NOT EVEN SURE ARE REAL MEMORIES.

THE LIFE IN DREAMS, THE LIFE THAT'S TAUGHT HIM THAT IT'S NOT ENOUGH TO FEEL ASHAMED OF BEING A PRICK...

I DON'T THINK YOU KNOW THE MEANING OF "WEIRD," ABBY.

...UNLESS YOU HAVE THE STRENGTH NOT TO *ACT* LIKE ONE.

THEN THAT ONLY PROVES MY POINT, MATT. YOU DON'T KNOW SHIT ABOUT ME. I DON'T THINK YOU EVER DID.

THE STRENGTH NOT TO WISH HELL ON PEOPLE FOR NOT LOVING YOU. HE THINKS HE HAD A FRIEND WHO DID THAT ONCE.

FOR REAL, OR IN A DREAM, IT DOESN'T MATTER.

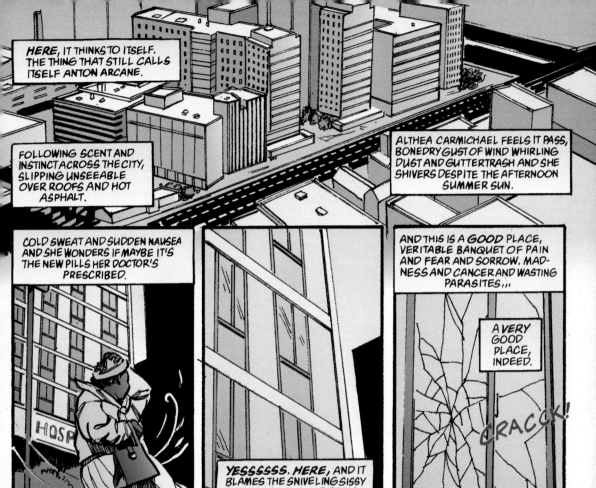

HERE, IT THINKS TO ITSELF. THE THING THAT STILL CALLS ITSELF ANTON ARCANE.

FOLLOWING SCENT AND INSTINCT ACROSS THE CITY, SLIPPING UNSEEABLE OVER ROOFS AND HOT ASPHALT.

ALTHEA CARMICHAEL FEELS IT PASS, BONEDRY GUST OF WIND WHIRLING DUST AND GUTTERTRASH AND SHE SHIVERS DESPITE THE AFTERNOON SUMMER SUN.

COLD SWEAT AND SUDDEN NAUSEA AND SHE WONDERS IF MAYBE IT'S THE NEW PILLS HER DOCTOR'S PRESCRIBED.

SHE CROSSES HERSELF WITHOUT THINKING WHY.

YESSSSSS. HERE, AND IT BLAMES THE SNIVELING SISSY BOY AGAIN, FOR THE SPELL GOING WRONG. PRECISION REQUIRES PURITY, AFTER ALL.

BUT IT WON'T MATTER MUCH LONGER. NOT IN THE END.

AND THIS IS A GOOD PLACE, VERITABLE BANQUET OF PAIN AND FEAR AND SORROW. MADNESS AND CANCER AND WASTING PARASITES...

A VERY GOOD PLACE, INDEED.

CRACCK!

OTHERS FEEL IT COMING, THE SICK AND DYING, THE MAD AND THE GRIEVING, SOMETHING FOCUSING THE BLUR OF THEIR SUFFERINGS.

SMASH!

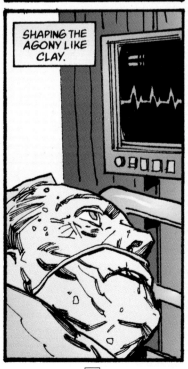

SHAPING THE AGONY LIKE CLAY.

GIVING ANGUISH A SINGLE, RASPING VOICE.

SOME LET GO, AND OTHERS HOLD ON AS IF THEIR SOULS DEPEND ON IT.

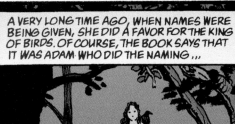

A VERY LONG TIME AGO, WHEN NAMES WERE BEING GIVEN, SHE DID A FAVOR FOR THE KING OF BIRDS. OF COURSE, THE BOOK SAYS THAT IT WAS ADAM WHO DID THE NAMING ...

...BUT THE BOOK SAYS A LOT OF THINGS.

THE KING OF BIRDS WAS VERY PROUD AND WANTED TO NAME *HIMSELF*. SO SHE LET HIM, AND LET HIM NAME ALL THE OTHER BIRDS, AS WELL.

SHE'S NEVER ASKED FOR ANYTHING IN RETURN.

BENEATH THESE TREES, EVE BEGINS TO CALL THEIR NAMES.

WARY EYES AND STRONG WINGS, RAINBOW OF FEATHERS, DAGGER BEAKS AND SICKLE CLAWS.

WEBBED TOES AND NERVOUS, PREENING BILLS.

SHE CALLS THEM ALL.

THE LEAST AMONG THEM...

...AND THE STILT-LEGGED BAYOU HUNTERS.

THE FISHERS AND SHORE-PICKERS.

CANDY SMUDGES OF COLOR AGAINST THE DULL SUMMER HEAT AND...

...THE PRINCES OF AIR.

SHE CALLS THEM ALL.

AND THEY COME TO HER.

AND FROM THE OLDEST STORIES KEPT IN THEIR SONGS (FOR BIRDS HAVE ALWAYS KEPT THEIR SECRETS IN SONG), THEY KNOW HER NAME, AND KNOW THEIR DEBT TO HER.

IT'S TRUE THEN... IT *IS* HER.

Well, shit on me.

HOW CAN WE BE SO SURE...

...THAT IT'S HER.

IT MIGHT BE ANOTHER WEARING HER FACE...

...AND VOICE. IT MIGHT BE A TRICK.

A COMMON WITCH TAKING US FOR NESTLINGS.

AN IMPOSTOR?

PRIDE UNDIMINISHED BY THE LONG AGES, AND SHE KNOWS THIS IS ALL BLUSTER, THAT THEY ARE AS OBLIGED TO RESIST AND BICKER AS THEY WERE TO RESPOND.

BUT SHE HAS NO PATIENCE FOR IT TODAY. AND LESS TIME...

YOU KNOW ME.

YES, mother of MAN, we know YOU.

MOTHER OF OUR MISERIES, YOU MEAN...

MOTHER OF ROASTING FIRES AND BULLETS.

...AND STINKING GRAY SKIES, MORE LIKE IT.

AN AWFUL LOT OF FUSS FROM BELLIES GROWN SO FAT ON THEIR GARBAGE...

IT'S ALL RIGHT, LUCIEN. IT HAS TO BE THIS WAY.

ENOUGH.

THEY'VE CHANGED AS LITTLE AS *MEN*, AS LITTLE AS ANYTHING ELSE *ALIVE*.

YOU *WOUND* US, TRULY.

WE HAVE NOT YET FORGOTTEN OURSELVES. *OR* OUR DEBT, OLD MOTHER.

FOREVER?

THEN I ASK ONE FAVOR IN RETURN AND THE SCORE WILL BE SETTLED.

FOREVER.

THEN ASK.

WE'RE WAITING.

I'M LOOKING FOR A RAVEN. NOT A LIVING RAVEN, BUT A *DREAM* RAVEN.

HIS NAME IS MATTHEW.

A *HUMAN* NAME, NO LESS.

ONE LACKEY'S NOT ENOUGH FOR HER, EH?

YOU SHOULD HOLD YOUR TONGUE, GULL, UNLESS PERHAPS YOU'D PREFER TO BE WITHOUT IT.

OOOOH. I AM SO SCARED.

IF YOUR DREAM RAVEN IS HERE, MOTHER OF MAN, WE WILL FIND HIM.

AND IF HE'S *NOT*, WE'RE JUST AS EVEN.

"WAIT HERE," THE OWL SAYS, AND THEY LEAVE HER, TWITTERING CLOUD OF FLESH AND BONE, SQUAWKING STORM OF BODIES RISING AS ONE TO BREAK APART OVERHEAD.

WILL THEY KEEP THEIR WORD?

IF HE'S HERE, THEY'LL FIND HIM. THEY'RE AN ARROGANT RACE, BUT THEY STILL HAVE HONOR, AND THEY'VE WAITED A LONG TIME TO ERASE THIS OBLIGATION....

I REALLY THINK I NEED TO SIT DOWN FOR A FEW MINUTES, LUCIEN.

AND SHE THINKS A MOMENT BEFORE SHE ANSWERS, WISHING SHE FELT EVEN THE SMALLEST RELIEF, WISHING FOR THE COMFORT OF HER CAVE, THE MURMURING COMFORT OF NIGHTMARES.

THE FUCKING BIRD'S BEEN THERE HALF AN HOUR NOW.

WANTING IN.

TAP TAP TAP TAP

TAP TAP TAP

TWO DAYS, ALMOST, SINCE THE GRAND FUCK-UP OF THE SUMMONING. TWO DAYS HE HASN'T SLEPT OR EATEN. PILLS TO STAY AWAKE, PILLS TO KEEP AWAY THE DREAMS.

AND NOW THIS GODDAMN BIRD.

TAP TAP TAP

HE'S LEARNED ENOUGH TO KNOW IT MEANS SOME-THING.

TAP TAP TAP TAP

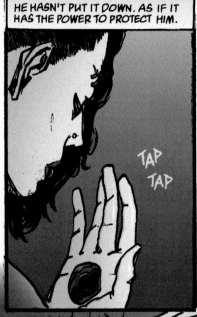

HE HASN'T PUT IT DOWN. AS IF IT HAS THE POWER TO PROTECT HIM.

TAP TAP

TAP TAP TAP

AS IF ANYTHING COULD.

TAP TAP TAP TAP TAP

THERE'S A SOUND OUTSIDE, LIKE RAIN, IF RAIN WAS FALLING AUTUMN LEAVES AND PLAYING CARDS AGAINST THE SPOKES OF SPINNING BICYCLE WHEELS.

HE LOOKS, BECAUSE IT WOULD BE WORSE NOT TO KNOW.

AND THE SKY IS MADE OF BIRDS.

END OF PART TWO

IT IS AN OLD CITY, AND NOT UNACCUSTOMED TO STRANGE THINGS. MORE THAN ITS SHARE FOR ONLY TWO HUNDRED AND SEVENTY-EIGHT YEARS.

ENOUGH HAUNTED PLACES AND BAD MEMORIES FOR *FIVE* CITIES, BUT SUCH EXPECTATIONS THAT THE TOURISTS ARE OBLIGED WITH CARDBOARD AND PASTE (TRUE PHANTOMS BEING TOO SHY FOR RELIABLE COMMERCE).

THE CHARADE, DEATH DRAG AND FUNERAL CAMP, AS MUCH A PART OF THE IMAGE AS FAT TUESDAY BEADS AND CRAWFISH BOILED CARNATION RED, AS MUCH THE PULSE OF THIS CITY.

BUT EVEN JADED NEW ORLEANS NOTICES WHEN, FROM TIME TO TIME, NATURE SKIPS A BEAT.

THE AUTHORITIES ARE BAFFLED AT THE SUDDEN APPEARANCE OF SO MANY BIRDS IN AUDUBON PARK THIS AFTERNOON.

SHIT. YOU SEE *THAT?*

...WHO SPOKE WITH DR. THORTON McGEHEE OF THE UNIVERSITY OF NEW ORLEANS, A NOTED ORNITHOLOGIST, ABOUT THE MYSTERIOUS GATHERING.

WHAT?

IT CERTAINLY IS UNUSUAL FOR SO MANY DIFFERENT SPECIES TO FLOCK TOGETHER.

LIKE IN THAT MOVIE, MAN.

ALL THEM BIRDS GONNA START *EATIN'* PEOPLE. YOU JUST WATCH AND SEE.

YOU'RE FULL OF SHIT, HENRY.

GODDAMN OZONE LAYER, YOU JUST WATCH.

...A SCIENTIFIC EXPLANATION, NO DOUBT.

AND THIS JUST IN, A DISTURBANCE AT CHARITY HOSPITAL THIS AFTERNOON, WE'RE TOLD THE AUTHORITIES HAVE THE SITUATION UNDER CONTROL...

YOU JUST WATCH. THEM HOLES GONNA DRIVE US ALL CRAZY.

...BUT STAY TUNED FOR DETAILS ON THIS BREAKING STORY...

HENRY, WHY DON'T YOU SHUT UP AND DRINK YOUR DAMN BEER.

Unkindness
of *One* & *part three*

Caitlin R. Kiernan, writer
Paul Lee, artist
Todd Klein, letterer
Daniel Vozzo, color & seps
Jennifer Lee, asst. ed.
Alisa Kwitney, editor
Neil Gaiman, consultant
The Dreaming created by
Neil Gaiman

IT WOULD *SEEM* THEY'VE FOUND HIM.

AND YES, SHE SAYS, BUT SHE STILL DOESN'T *FEEL* HIM, AND HOPES IT'S ONLY DISTRACTION, THE COMMOTION OF WINGS AND TAUNTING BIRD VOICES OVER-HEAD.

THEIR BODIES BLOCK THE SWELTERING DELTA SUN, AND THEIR SHIT FALLS LIKE LAZY WHITE RAIN.

THEY'VE CERTAINLY FOUND *SOMETHING*. I DO RATHER WISH WE HAD THOUGHT TO BRING...

CREEAK

...AN UMBRELLA.

SPLAT

IT'S NOT LOCKED.

IT DOESN'T LOOK AS IF ANYONE'S LIVED HERE FOR QUITE SOME TIME.

THEN SHE *DOES* FEEL HIM, THE DIMMEST FAINT FLICKER OF HIM HIDDEN IN THE STALE AIR THE HOUSE BREATHES OUT; DUST AND MILDEW AND THE STINGY HINT OF MATTHEW.

ARE YOU *SURE?* I DON'T FEEL ANYTHING BUT...

SHHHH.

AND SHE SHIVERS, GOOSE BUMPS AND A COLDER SHIVER DOWN INSIDE HER, THE SUDDEN SHADOW OF THE HOUSE AFTER SO MUCH SUN, AND THE NEW EDGE TO HER DREAD, THAT HE COULD FEEL AT ONCE SO CLOSE AND FAR AWAY.

SAFE FROM THE SHATTERED WINDOW LEFT BY ARCANE'S DEPARTURE, THE DOOR TO THAT ROOM CLOSED TIGHT AND LOCKED, BUT A HUNDRED OTHER PLACES TO GET IN, IF SOMETHING IS DETERMINED.

HE IMAGINES THE BIRDS ARE *ALREADY* IN THE HOUSE, LOOKING FOR HIM.

ECHO'S NOT ENTIRELY SURE WHAT HE EXPECTED, SO HE COULDN'T SAY THIS IS *UNEXPECTED.*

A CONSEQUENCE OF HIS FAILURE WITH THE SUMMONING, PERHAPS, OR MAYBE THIS WOMAN'S BEEN SENT BY THE THING THAT CALLED ITSELF ARCANE, SOMEONE SENT TO SNIP A LOOSE END.

BUT THE RAVEN ON HER SHOULDER...THE *RAVEN* HE REMEMBERS.

HE'S BEEN THINKING ABOUT JUST KILLING HIMSELF WHILE THERE'S STILL TIME.

TOO SICK OF MISSING GABE, TOO SICK OF BEING AFRAID AND FEELING LIKE AN ASS AND A FUCK-UP.

BUT HE'S PRETTY SURE DEATH'S NO GUARANTEE AGAINST REVENGE, AND NOW THE RAVEN...

THE RAVEN THE CORINTHIAN CALLED MATTHEW, *SURELY* THE SAME RAVEN.

HE STOPPED BELIEVING IN COINCIDENCES SOME TIME BACK.

SO MAYBE THE SPELL *DIDN'T* FALL SO SHORT OF ITS INTENDED MARK AFTER ALL.

AND MAYBE THERE'S A REASON TO LIVE A LITTLE WHILE LONGER.

C'MON, BITCH. LET'S GET THIS OVER WITH.

ONE WAY OR ANOTHER, HE WON'T HAVE TO WAIT LONG TO FIND OUT.

CHARITY HOSPITAL.

ALMOST TEN MINUTES NOW SINCE IT STARTED, THE LAUGHTER AND SCREAMING FROM THE DAY ROOM. THE SOMETHING WRONG THAT SHE'LL LEARN, LATER ON, HAS SPREAD LIKE BAD AIR UP FROM THE FLOORS BELOW, SLIPPING FROM ROOM TO ROOM TO ROOM.

GATHERING PAIN AND SICKNESS...

GATHERING MADNESS...

I DON'T GIVE A SHIT, CHARLIE. SOMEONE'S GONNA GET HURT IF WE DON'T HAVE SOME HELP UP HERE FAST.

GATHERING ITSELF.

IT'S TIME FOR ME TO GO NOW, MATT. WE'LL TALK AGAIN SOON, OKAY? MAYBE WHEN YOU'RE FEELING BETTER, WHEN YOU'RE STRONGER.

ABBY, I'M SO SORRY...

THERE'S NOTHING TO BE SORRY ABOUT. IT'S JUST THE WAY THINGS HAPPENED.

JESUS, HE WANTS TO BELIEVE HER, AND HE WISHES HE COULD STOP CRYING, WISHES THERE WAS ANYTHING HE COULD SAY TO MAKE HER STAY.

ANYTHING HE COULD DO.

"YOU HAVE TO STOP BLAMING YOURSELF. SOMETIMES SHIT JUST HAPPENS, YOU KNOW?"

...FOR SO MANY DIFFERENT SPECIES TO FLOCK TOGETHER.

SHIT HAPPENS AND WE GET CAUGHT IN THE MIDDLE.

WE ALWAYS HAVE TO THINK IT'S OUR FAULT SO IT MAKES SOME KIND OF SENSE.

YOU'LL BE OKAY, MATT CABLE. HELL, IF YOU CAN COME BACK FROM THE DEAD...

ABBY, I SWEAR, IT DOESN'T HAVE TO BE LIKE THIS.

IT ALREADY IS LIKE THIS, MATT.

GOD, HE LOVES HER SO MUCH. HE STILL LOVES HER SO MUCH AND THERE'S NOTHING BUT THE SOUND OF HER WALKING AWAY.

THE SOUND OF LOSING HER AGAIN.

AND THEN IT'S BACK AGAIN, SO SUDDEN AND STRONG THAT THE TASTE AND SMELL OF IT MAKE HIM GAG. SO ANGRY AND BRUISED IT ONLY WANTS TO WOUND, ONLY WANTS TO PASS THE HURT ALONG.

AND HE TRIES TO WARN HER.

MATT, THE DOOR'S LOCKED...

OPENS HIS MOUTH TO SAY THE WORDS, WATCH OUT, BUT IT'S ALREADY TOO LATE.

LUCIEN, WAIT...

LUCIEN? MATTHEW?

THERE'S A SOUR COLD-NESS TO THIS PLACE, AND SHE'S ALMOST AFRAID TO GO ANY FURTHER. WANTS TO TURN AND RUN BACK OUT INTO THE SUN, BACK TO THE SHADOWS OF HER CAVE.

SHE IS OLD AS THE FEAR OF MAN, AND IT'S BEEN A VERY LONG TIME SINCE SHE'S BEEN AFRAID.

LUCIEN, WHERE *ARE* YOU?

WE'RE RIGHT HERE, YOU STUPID FUCKING HIPPIE.

THIS BIRD AND ME, WE HAVE SOME UNFINISHED BUSINESS. AIN'T THAT *RIGHT*, BIRD?

I'M QUITE CERTAIN THAT I'VE NEVER SEEN YOU IN MY ENTIRE LIFE.

I THINK YOU'RE MAKING A MISTAKE.

YEAH? WELL, MAYBE SO, LADY.

BUT I THINK IT WAS THIS FUCKING BIRD THAT MADE THE *MISTAKE*. LIKE I WOULDN'T REMEMBER HE WAS THE ONE THAT HELPED THAT *BASTARD* GET GABE...

A REALLY *BIG* MISTAKE.

SQUAWK!

THIS IS *NOT* THE RAVEN MATTHEW. *THIS* IS THE RAVEN LUCIEN.

WE'VE COME FOR THE RAVEN MATTHEW.

WHERE IS HE?

YOU CAN SUCK MY DICK, BITCH.

LISTEN TO ME, LITTLE *BOY*. I DON'T KNOW EXACTLY *WHAT* YOU *THINK* YOU WERE TRYING TO DO. AND RIGHT NOW I DON'T *CARE...*

YOU'RE ALREADY IN SO FAR OVER YOUR PRETTY LITTLE EMPTY HEAD, BUT I *PROMISE* YOU, CHILD, IT CAN GET A *LOT WORSE* FOR YOU IF I WANT IT TO.

I KNOW HE'S HERE SOMEWHERE.

SO I'M GOING TO START COUNTING...

EVE, I THINK PERHAPS YOU SHOULD HAVE A LOOK AT THIS.

NOT COLD WHEN SHE TOUCHED IT, BUT GOING COLD IN HER HAND, FLASHING COLD THAT BURNS BEFORE SHE CAN PULL AWAY.

OH GOD, MATT...

AND WHEN SHE DOES TAKE HER HAND AWAY, THERE'S A SOFT TEARING SOUND AND SHE LEAVES SKIN BEHIND.

LIVING CORRUPTION THAT STINKS LIKE A ROTTING FRUIT STAND, LIKE GREASY SUMMER ROADKILL, SICKSWEET, GASSY, AND THEN IT TOUCHES HER.

AND IT FEELS THE WAY IT SMELLS.

EXACTLY.

ABBY!

YOU STAY THE FUCK *AWAY* FROM HER!

TELL ME WHAT THE HELL'S HAPPENING, MATT!

YESSSSS, MATT. TELL HER. *PLEASSSSE* TELL HER WHAT THE HELL'SSSS HAPPENING...

BUT THAT'S THE WORST, THE SOUND IT MAKES, A SOUND THE SAME AS THE SMELL, AS THE TOUCH.

THAT'S THE VERY WORST.

YOU CAN SPEAK FOR YOURSELF, ANTON *ARCANE.*

MAYBE YOU HAVEN'T BEEN LISTENING...

OW!

...SO I'LL SAY IT AGAIN.

IT CAN GET A LOT WORSE.

NO...

OH YES.

BLAM!

THINGS ARE NEVER AS BAD AS THEY *CAN* BE, CHILD.

STOP, YOU IDIOTS!

THIS WASN'T PART OF THE DEAL.

"AND SHE SHED OUR BLOOD, EVEN WHILE WE WERE KEEPING OUR WORD."

THE GULL'S RIGHT, MOTHER OF MAN. THE OLD SCORE IS SETTLED.

OH, BUT HE *DOES* LOOK TASTY, DON'T HE?

OH GOD, PLEASE...

YES, WE'RE EVEN. AND I'M GRATEFUL, OWL.

YOUR RACE STILL HAS HONOR.

"FARE WELL, THEN, OLD MOTHER," THE OWL SAYS, AND THEY LEAVE HER ...

WITH HER PART IN THIS STILL UNFINISHED.

AND SHE WISHES THAT IT WAS SOMETHING SHE COULD DO ALONE, WISHES SHE WERE THAT STRONG, THAT CLEVER, THAT CERTAIN OF HERSELF.

SHE HAS NO *RIGHT* TO DO THIS, ONLY THE NEED. THE NEED WILL HAVE TO DO. THERE WILL BE TIME ENOUGH FOR REGRET LATER.

THERE ALWAYS HAS BEEN.

FROM THE LONG CATALOGUE OF HER DEAD, FORGOTTEN FACES AND HALF-REMEMBERED NAMES, BUT *THESE* KEPT LIKE JEWELS, LIKE CHARMS AGAINST OBLIVION.

KEEP AN EYE ON HIM, PLEASE, LUCIEN.

THE NAMES OF THE RAVENS OF THE DREAMING, AND *FORGIVE ME*, SHE SAYS, AND IT BEGINS.

HATSHEPSUT, ARISTEAS...

...DECHTIRE, MING-TI, VIVIEN...

...JEHUDA, FRANÇOIS...

...JESSAMY...

FORGIVE ME.

NO, MATT, THIS IS **IMPOSSIBLE!** YOU DON'T UNDERSTAND, YOU'RE NOT LISTENING TO ME.

THINGS HAVE **CHANGED. EVERYTHING'S** CHANGED.

HIS HEAD IS BEGINNING TO HURT, AND THAT'S WORSE THAN THE PILLS. CONCENTRATION LIKE SWIMMING UPSTREAM AND EVERYTHING DEPENDS ON IT.

YOU'RE WRONG,,,

YESSSSSSS, ABIGAILLLLL, WRRRONGGG! AND THISSSS TIMMME YOU'RRE MINNNNE FOREVERRRR...

BUT HE KNOWS WHAT HE HAS TO DO.

MATT, THIS SHIT IS **NOT MY UNCLE.**

I DON'T KNOW WHAT'S HAPPENING, BUT THIS HAS NOTHING TO DO WITH **HIM.**

IT'S A SIMPLE THING; HE COULD DO IT IN HIS **SLEEP,** COULD DO IT WITH HIS EYES FUCKING CLOSED.

BACCCK TO HELLLL, ABIGAILLLLLLLL ...

THIS TIME HE'S HERE FOR HER, AND ALL HE HAS TO DO IS IMAGINE,,,

MATT, DID YOU DO THAT?

,,,AND MAKE THE BAD THING GO AWAY.

HE'S NOT GONNA TOUCH YOU **THIS** TIME, ABBY. THIS TIME THE SON-OF-A-BITCH ISN'T EVEN GONNA **TOUCH** YOU.

JESUS, MATT,,, THIS JUST CAN'T BE HAPPENING.

HE FOLLOWS THEM FROM THE SHABBY OLD HOUSE, INSUBSTANTIAL AND ABSOLUTE PHANTOMS OF ALL THE ONES THAT CAME AFTER THE FLOOD, AFTER HIM.

IT HURTS THEM TO BE HERE, DEAD AMONG THE LIVING.

HE WOULD HAVE TRIED TO STOP HER FROM CALLING THEM, IF HE'D THOUGHT SHE WOULD HAVE LISTENED, WOULD EVEN HAVE HEARD.

HATSHEPSUT, NILE QUEEN TO THE DREAM OF A RAVEN AND NOW THE GHOST OF A DREAM, AND EVEN SHE ONLY COUGHED HER SAND-DRY COUGH AND LOOKED AT LUCIEN AS IF THERE WERE SOME WAY HE MIGHT SEND THEM BACK TO THE MERCY OF THEIR OBLIVIONS.

"BRING HIM BACK TO ME," EVE SAID, UNDENIABLE.

"FIND HIM," SHE SAID. "PLEASE,,," AND PERFECT SABLE SILENCE FROM THEM ALL, EXCEPT HATSHEPSUT.

HIS MIND RACING LIKE THE WIND LOUD ACROSS HIS FEATHERS, FLIPPING PAGES BACK AND BACK AND HE KNOWS.

EVE HAS LAID HER FINGER ON THE SCALES, ANOTHER VIOLATION IN A LONG AND WARPING STRAND OF WRONGS.

"HE'S HERE," CAWS JEHUDA SOMEWHERE BELOW. "HE'S HERE."

HOSPITAL

A CENTURY OF WRONGS. A CENTURY ALMOST PAST, AND THE BILL WILL COME DUE, THE LIBRARIAN THINKS.

HE SHIVERS AS HE PASSES THROUGH THEIR SOULS.

MATTTT CABBBB-LLLLLE...

TEN YEARS HIDING OUT IN DREAMS, SHRILL SIDEKICK FOR A PHANTASM, ERRAND BOY (ERRAND *BIRD*, MATT) FOR SHABBY ARCHETYPES.

CRUSSSSSHHH YOU, CABBBLLE. MAAAKE YOUU PAAAAAYYY...

HE REMEMBERS BELIEVING ALL THIS SHIT WAS *BEHIND* HIM. SECOND CHANCE, CLEAN AND SIMPLE.

IT WANTS IN (*OUT*, IT WANTS OUT), AND HE HEARS A SOUND LIKE LIGHT MIGHT MAKE, IF LIGHT COULD CRACK, COULD SPLINTER. IF LIGHT WERE THE THIN BONES OF HIS SKULL.

I'VE BEEN THROUGH TOO MUCH TO GET EATEN ALIVE BY A PISSED-OFF *OILSLICK*.

THE BLACKNESS IN (FROM, MATT, *FROM*) HIS HEAD FESTERS AND STARTS TO WHINE, HOT SOUND, STRIPPED GEARS, BROKEN MACHINE WAIL.

SOMETHING TEARING ITSELF APART...

I'M *NOT* DYING IN HERE, MATT.

CAN YOU *HEAR* ME? CAN YOU UNDERSTAND A *WORD* OF THIS?

...TOOO HELLLL, ABIGAILLLL, BACCCKKK TOOOO HELLLLLL...

LEAVE ME ALONE!

TEARING HIM APART.

AND THEN THE SOUND OF THEIR WINGS, NOT WINGS THROUGH AIR, BUT TIME.

AND HE KNOWS THEM, THOUGH THEY'VE NEVER MET, AND THEY KNOW *HIM*.

THEY ARE *HELPLESS*.

SUDDENLY SO SIMPLE HE COULD LAUGH, IF THERE WERE ANY LAUGHTER LEFT IN HIM, ANYTHING BUT FREEZING, LIVING LOSS AND GUILT.

NO ROOM LEFT TO HOLD IT IN ...

SO HE LETS IT OUT.

WE CANNOT FIGHT *THIS*. WE CANNOT HURT THE ONE SHE'S SENT US TO SAVE.

I KNOW, JESSAMY, BUT...

HE'LL DESTROY US, LUCIEN.

LUCIEN...?

AND THE REPLY IN HIS HEAD, THEN...

YES, MATTHEW, AND *YOU* HAVE TO STOP THIS...

...BARELY GETTING IN, ANOTHER'S THOUGHTS SHREDDED BUT SQUEEZING THROUGH...

YOU'RE ONLY FIGHTING YOURSELF, AND HE WISHES HE DIDN'T HAVE TO HEAR, DIDN'T HAVE TO BELIEVE.

YOU HAVE TO STOP THIS NOW.

BUT... I'M ALIVE, LUCIEN.

STOP THIS *NOW*, MATTHEW!

CAW!

I'M A MAN AGAIN...

AS EASY AS OPENING HIS EYES...

SO, FROM HERE ON OUT, ABUDAH IS STRICTLY LANDSCAPIN' AND STABLE MUCKIN'.

THAT'S VERY REASSURING, MERVYN.

WELL, YA KNOW I'D LOVE TO STAND 'ROUND HERE AND CHEW THE FAT ALL DAY LONG, BUT I GOTTA SPLIT.

GOTTA SEE TO A NEW DREDGING JOB, AND THE WORK SURE DON'T DO ITSELF.

HE WAITS UNTIL THE JANITOR HAS GONE, NOTHING LEFT BUT TOBACCO SMOKE AND THE SLUGSLICK SMELL OF OLD PUMPKIN.

BEFORE HE LOOKS AT IT AGAIN.

HE'D ALMOST FORGOTTEN IT, TUCKED AWAY IN A NEGLECTED CORNER TOO MUSTY FOR EVEN THE SPIDERS AND SILVERFISH.

FILED BETWEEN THE BEGINNINGS OF UNFINISHED BUSINESS AND LOST LOVES (FOR THEY BOTH BEGIN AT THE SAME PLACE AND LEAD IN OPPOSITE DIRECTIONS).

HE'S READ IT EVERY DAY SINCE COMING BACK TO HIS LIBRARY AND THE SKIN AND BONES OF A MAN.

"...a shallow hole in the earth," the raven said to her, "but make it deep enough that the jackals won't come and dig him up again. And a cairn of stones on top, against the lions..."

"DIG A HOLE IN THE GROUND," THE RAVEN SAID, "A HOLE BIG ENOUGH TO HOLD HIS REMAINS, BUT BE SURE THAT IT'S DEEP ENOUGH THAT THE WILD BEASTS WON'T DIG HIM UP AGAIN."

AND THEN THE RAVEN SHOWED HER HOW TO COVER THE GRAVE WITH STONES...

MATTHEW? ARE YOU ASLEEP?

HE HAS THIS DREAM SOME- TIMES...

HE KNOWS THAT IT'S ONLY A DREAM, BECAUSE IN IT, HE'S A MAN, STILL OR AGAIN. THAT PART DOESN'T MATTER.

HIS ARM THRUST DOWN AND DOWN, THROUGH COLD LIKE BLUE-WHITE EMBERS AND ACID.

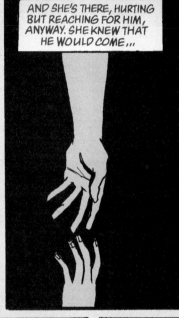

AND SHE'S THERE, HURTING BUT REACHING FOR HIM, ANYWAY. SHE KNEW THAT HE WOULD COME...

HIS HAND CLOSES FIRM AROUND HER WRIST, WARMTH FLOWING FROM HIS PALM INTO HER, AND HE PULLS HER UP.

AND SOMETIMES THE WOMAN'S NAME IS ABIGAIL, AND OTHER TIMES HER NAME IS EVE. THAT PART DOESN'T REALLY MATTER, EITHER.

THAT'S ALL RIGHT. YOU KNOW HOW IT TURNS OUT.

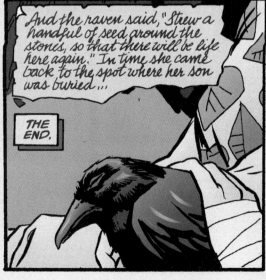

And the raven said, "Strew a handful of seed around the stones, so that there will be life here again." In time she came back to the spot where her son was buried...

THE END.

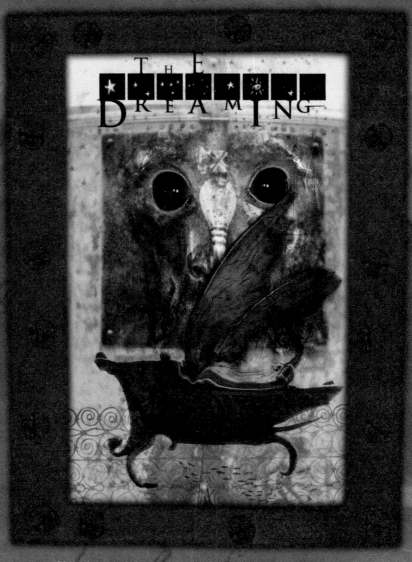

"My Year As A Man"

MY YEAR AS A MAN

PETER HOGAN: WRITER
CHRIS WESTON: ARTIST
TODD KLEIN: LETTERS
DANIEL VOZZO: COLOR+SEPS
JENNIFER LEE: ASST. ED.
ALISA KWITNEY: EDITOR
NEIL GAIMAN: CONSULTS
THE DREAMING CREATED
BY NEIL GAIMAN

AWRRK?

YES, I KNUH-KNUH-*KNOW*...

IT'S FUH-*FOOLISH* OF ME.

IT'S JUH-JUST WHENEVER IT'S TUH-TUH *TEATIME*, I KEEP THINKING, "MUH-MATTHEW'S GOING TO FUH-FLAP THROUGH THE WUH-WINDOW ANY SUH-SECOND NOW"...

...BUT HE NEVER DUH-DOES.

AND I MUH-MUH-*MISS* HIM. I HAVEN'T GUH-*GOT* THAT MANY FUH-FRIENDS, AND...

FUH-FIRST GUH-*GOLDIE*, AND NOW MUH-*MATTHEW* ...ALL MY FUH-FRIENDS SUH-SEEM TO BE GUH-GOING *AWAY*...

PUH-PUH-*PRESENT* COMPANY *EXSUHCEPTED*, OF CUH-*COURSE*.

NOW WHAT ARE YOU WITTERING ABOUT?

I WAS JUST WUH-WONDERING WHEN MUH-*MATTHEW* WILL COME BUH-*BACK*...

PAH. WHO *CARES*?

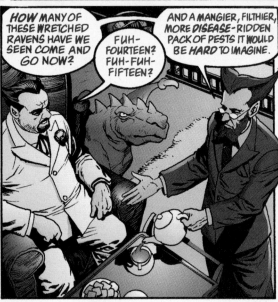

HOW MANY OF THESE WRETCHED RAVENS HAVE WE SEEN COME AND GO NOW?

FUH-*FOURTEEN*? FUH-FUH-*FIFTEEN*?

AND A MANGIER, FILTHIER, MORE *DISEASE*-RIDDEN PACK OF PESTS IT WOULD BE *HARD* TO IMAGINE.

BUT FOR SOME *BIZARRE* REASON HE SEEMS TO *LIKE* THEM.

SO, I DARESAY THERE'LL BE *ANOTHER* ONE ALONG ANY MINUTE...

HERE-- TAKE YOUR *TEA*.

THUH-*THANK* YOU.

SANDWICH? *CAKE*?

NO, THUH-THANK YOU. I'M NOT RUH-REALLY HUH-*HUNGRY*...

AFTER I SPENT *HOURS* PREPARING THEM?

AND THEY LUH-LUH-LOOK *DELICIOUS.*

NOW THAT I THUH-*THINK* OF IT, I'M PUH-*POSITIVELY FAMISHED.*

I SUPPOSE THE BLASTED BIRD PROBABLY *WILL* COME CRAWLING BACK AGAIN, JUST LIKE...

WHAT WAS HIS NAME? THE TEDIOUS *POETIC* ONE?

ARISTEAS OF MUH-MUH-*MARMORA.* YES... HE DUH-*DID* COME BUH-*BACK,* DIDN'T HE?

BUT WUH-WUH-*WHY* DID HE?

I NEITHER REMEMBER NOR *GIVE A DAMN.*

IF YOU'RE *THAT* CURIOUS, I SUGGEST YOU GO AND LOOK IT *UP.*

THE DREAM TIMES

HOWL! WEREWOLF ON LOOSE IN LONDON

WHAT A GUH-*GOOD* IDEA, CAIN.

I BUH-BELIEVE I SHUH-*SHALL.*

AFTER I'VE FUH-FINISHED *EATING,* OF CUH-COURSE...

RRRRFF.

THE LIBRARY OF DREAM, SOME HOURS LATER.

LUH-LUH-*LUCIEN*...

Hmmmn?

I CAN'T FUH-FIND *ANYTHING* BUH-BY *ARISTEAS* OF MUH-MARMORA,...

...AND I'VE LUH-LOOKED RIGHT *THROUGH* THE PUH-PUH-POETRY SHELVES.

AH, THAT'S BECAUSE HE'S FILED UNDER *"CLASSICS."*

OH.

WELL, I WUH-WANTED TO KNUH-KNOW ABOUT HIS RUH-RETURN TO THE WUH-WUH-*WAKING* WORLD,...

THEN I *THINK* YOU'RE IN LUCK.

ARISTEAS *MEANT* TO WRITE A MEMOIR OF HIS TRAVELS, BUT OF COURSE ONCE HE WAS A RAVEN AGAIN, HE FOR-GOT ALL ABOUT IT,...

FORTUNATELY, THE LIBRARY *DIDN'T*. AH, HERE IT IS,...

I THINK *THIS* IS WHAT YOU'RE LOOKING FOR,...

"MY YEAR AS A MUH-MUH-MAN",...

BY ARISTEAS OF MUH-MAR-MORA.

"GENTLE RUH– READERS...."

GENTLE READERS....

YOU SHOULD KNOW THAT I HAD SERVED MY MASTER FAITHFULLY AND WELL FOR TWO HUNDRED AND FORTY YEARS, AS TIME IS RECKONED ON EARTH, WHEN THERE CAME UPON ME A RESTLESSNESS OF SPIRIT...

I KNEW NOT WHY, FULLY, BUT I YEARNED FOR THINGS LONG LOST TO ME AND THOUGHT FORGOTTEN...

THE TASTE OF CERTAIN FOODS, THE ARDOR OF HUMAN LOVE, THE FEEL OF SEA SPRAY ON MY SKIN... ON THESE MEMORIES AND MORE I BROODED.

BUT MY LORD GUESSED MY HEART'S SECRET, AND NOBLY OFFERED TO GRANT ITS DESIRE. STILL, HE COUNSELLED CAUTION, AND MADE WITH ME A COMPACT:

IF THE WORLD OF MEN SUITED ME NOT, I SHOULD RETURN TO HIS SIDE WITHIN A YEAR AND A DAY, OR ELSE REMAIN A MAN FOR MY MORTAL LIFETIME.

AND TO THIS, I READILY AGREED.

AND I AWOKE UNDER A TREE, IN MY HUMAN SHAPE AND CLAD IN FINE RAIMENT, WITH A FULL PURSE OF GOLD AT MY SIDE...

FOR MY MASTER WAS EVER GENEROUS.

"SLEEP, THEN," SAID HE, AND I DID AS I WAS BID.

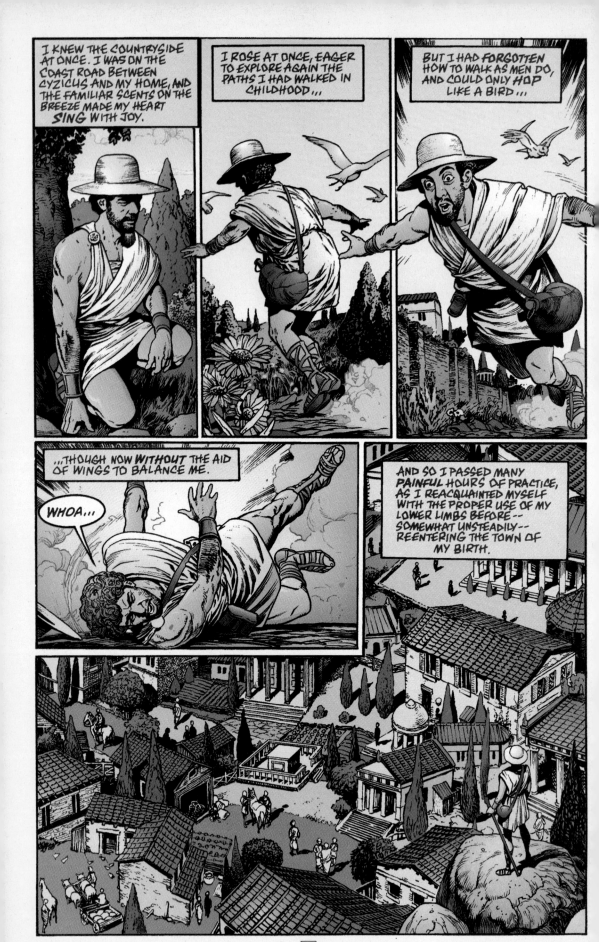

LITTLE HAD CHANGED THERE, AND EACH STEP I TOOK AWOKE WITHIN ME THE CHILD WHO HAD ONCE PLAYED IN THESE STREETS...

...YET THERE WERE ALSO *NEWER* BUILDINGS THAT I DID *NOT* KNOW, STANDING WHERE THERE HAD ONCE BEEN ONLY MEADOWLANDS.

I TOOK A ROOM AT THE TAVERN, THEN SOUGHT OUT MY PARENTS' HOUSE. IT WAS EASILY FOUND, BUT THE SIGHT OF IT BROUGHT ONLY *SORROW*...

...FOR THEIR SPIRITS HAD DEPARTED AN *AGE AGO*, AND *STRANGERS* NOW DWELT WITHIN THOSE BELOVED WALLS.

THE FAMILIAR *MOCKED* ME AT EVERY TURN. EVEN THE FACES OF THOSE I SAW ON THE STREETS AND IN THE TAVERN ECHOED THOSE OF THEIR FORE-FATHERS, SO THAT HERE I SAW A FRIEND, THERE AN *ENEMY*...

THOUGH IN TRUTH, ALL WERE STRANGERS TO ME, AND MY HOME WAS HOME NO LONGER.

AND I HAD THOUGHT THAT HERE AT LEAST, MY WORK WOULD BE REMEMBERED. BUT THOUGH SOME KNEW MY TALE, NONE SAVE A FEW SCHOLARS RECALLED THE TELLER'S NAME...

...AND SO I LEFT THAT PLACE FOR THE LAST TIME, AND WALKED OUT INTO THE WIDER WORLD.

AS I HAD ALREADY EXPLORED THE NORTHERN LANDS, THIS TIME I JOURNEYED SOUTH, MY THOUGHT BEING TO WRITE AN ACCOUNT OF THESE TRAVELS...

...AND SO EIGHT MONTHS PASSED UNEVENTFULLY, AS I STUDIED THE CURIOUS BELIEFS OF THOSE REGIONS, BEFORE FINALLY *TIRING* OF SAND AND SUPERSTITION.

WITH LITTLE TIME REMAINING TO ME, AND LONGING ONLY FOR GREENERY AND GOOD FOOD, FOR CONVIVIAL COMPANY AND A PLEASANT CLIMATE, I TOOK SHIP AT THE NEAREST PORT, AND SAILED FOR *OENOTRIA*.

LUH-LUCIEN? WUH-WHERE'S *OENOTRIA*?

ER... IF I REMEMBER *CORRECTLY*, IT WAS A GREEK COLONY IN SOUTHERN ITALY... SEVENTH CENTURY B.C., OR THEREABOUTS.

OH, HOW I LONGED TO BE ABLE TO FLY ONCE AGAIN--TO GLIDE EFFORTLESSLY *ABOVE* THE EARTH, INSTEAD OF BEING FORCED TO CRAWL ACROSS ITS SURFACE...

...AND SAILING WAS EVEN *WORSE*. ONLY A *FOOL* WOULD DO THIS BY CHOICE.

≶WEEURGHH≶

YOU ALL RIGHT, SIR?

BEEN FEEDIN' THE *BIRDS*, HAVE YOU?

I'M ≶urp≶ *FINE*...

...OR I *WILL* BE, WHEN THIS *STORM* SUBSIDES.

WHY, *BLESS* YOU, SIR--*THIS* ISN'T A STORM.

THE WAVES JUST GOT A BIT O' *BOUNCE* IN 'EM, THAT'S ALL...

NOW, YOU SEE *THEM?* THOSE DARK CLOUDS ON THE HORIZON?

YES...

THAT'S A STORM.

AND HEADED OUR WAY, BY THE LOOK OF HER...

SCARCE HAD HE SPOKEN--OR SO IT SEEMED TO ME-- WHEN THE TEMPEST WAS *UPON* US, AND WE WERE CAUGHT IN THE FULL FURY OF ITS BLAST...

AS IF POSEIDON HIMSELF WERE WAGING *WAR,* AND WE HAD STRAYED ALL UNKNOWING UPON THE *BATTLEFIELD.*

MASTLESS AND CRIPPLED, OUR SHIP WAS DRIVEN *MANY* LEAGUES OFF COURSE... UNTIL FINALLY, IT FOUNDERED UPON THE ROCKS...

...I WANTED LAND BENEATH MY FEET AGAIN FOR A WHILE, AND SO RESUMED MY JOURNEY ON FOOT.

I FOUND MYSELF SHIPWRECKED, UPON THE SHORE OF *THESSALY*...

BEFORE LONG I HAD REACHED NEARBY *MOUNT PELION,* WHERE A FIGURE OUT OF LEGEND AWAITED ME...

HAIL, ARISTEAS...

THOUGH THE CAPTAIN ASSURED ME HIS SHIP COULD BE REPAIRED...

I THOUGHT,...THAT IS, I HEARD YOU WERE *DEAD*-- AND THAT *ALL* THE CENTAURS HAD *VANISHED* FROM THE WORLD...

BELIEFS I HAVE *CULTIVATED*, FOR THEY SUITED MY PURPOSE.

FORTUNATELY-- AND THANKS TO *YOUR* KIND, POET-- WHEN MEN SEE CENTAURS PINNED DOWN UPON A PAGE, THEY THINK THEM ONLY *TRAVELLERS'* *TALES*...

THOUGH, IN TRUTH, OUR AGE *HAS* PASSED, AND MY PEOPLE HAVE SOUGHT *OTHER* WORLDS IN WHICH TO DWELL.

SOMEDAY, I MUST JOIN THEM, BUT,...THERE IS STILL SO MUCH TO BE *DONE* HERE...

AH, *HERE* WE ARE...

I HOPE YOU ARE *HUNGRY*, AFTER YOUR TRAVELS.

ER,...YES, I AM. *VERY*.

GOOD.

I HOPE MY REMARKS ABOUT YOUR PROFESSION CAUSED NO OFFENSE?

FOR I MYSELF *APPRECIATE* A GOOD STORY, AND DID GREATLY *ENJOY* YOUR "TALE OF THE ARIMASPIANS."

YOU'VE *READ* IT?

A *LONG* TIME AGO-- BUT I REMEMBER IT FONDLY.

"THOSE SHIFTLESS ONE-EYED MEN, FOREVER TRYING --AND COMICALLY *FAILING*-- TO STEAL THE GOLD FROM THE RIVER GUARDED BY WATCHFUL *GRYPHONS*...

"THE *'HOUNDS OF ZEUS'* YOU CALLED THEM. A FINE TURN OF PHRASE, I THOUGHT."

THOUGH, AS I RECALL, YOU DID NOT ACTUALLY JOURNEY TO ARIMASPIA YOURSELF?

NO. I *HEARD* THE TALE, FROM THE ISSEDONIANS...

...BUT I *DID* LATER KNOW A GRYPHON, WHO BECAME A DEAR FRIEND OF MINE...

I SHOULD DEARLY *LOVE* TO SEE SUCH A CREATURE... BUT ARIMASPIA RECEDES FURTHER FROM THIS WORLD, AND THE JOURNEY IS NOW A *LONG* ONE. *SOMEDAY*, PERHAPS...

THANK YOU, SOLON. YOU MAY RETURN TO YOUR STUDIES NOW.

YOUR LATEST CHARGE?

YES. A GOOD LAD. I TEACH HIM AGRICULTURE, AND ARCHERY...

AND IDEAS.

MOST OF *ALL*, IDEAS...

WHICH REMINDS ME -- IF I READ THE STARS ARIGHT, ARE YOU NOT THE MESSENGER OF *ONEIROS?*

I AM.

THAT IS, I *WAS*...MY LORD HAS GRACIOUSLY GRANTED ME A LEAVE OF ABSENCE, TO...TRAVEL.

THAT EXPLAINS YOUR HUMAN SHAPE, NO DOUBT. I *HAD* BEEN EXPECTING A RAVEN, NATURALLY...AND ALSO A *MESSAGE?*

I'M AFRAID NOT. NOT BY *MY* HAND.

212

AH WELL, DOUBTLESS HE SENDS ANOTHER...

A THANKLESS TASK, MESSENGERING FOR THE GREAT, I HAVE ALWAYS FELT.

THE FIRST RAVEN WAS WHITE, SO THEY SAY,... UNTIL HE BROUGHT NEWS OF HIS MASTER'S LOVE'S UNFAITHFULNESS, AND WAS TURNED BLACK FOR HIS TROUBLE...

I AM SURE YOU HAVE EARNED YOUR REST, AND LOOK FORWARD TO READING THE ACCOUNT OF THIS JOURNEY.

YOUR PATH TAKES YOU ON, THROUGH THESSALY?

YES, RIGHT THROUGH...

THEN BE CAREFUL, POET...

THIS COUNTRY IS NOT WHAT IT WAS.

THOUGH I KNEW HE MEANT WELL, I PAID CHIRON'S WARNING BUT LITTLE HEED--FOR I WAS ACCUSTOMED TO THE PROTECTION OF MY MASTER, AND THUS FEARED NO MAN...

BUT OTHERS I MET UPON THE ROAD ALSO SPOKE OF DANGER.

AS YOU LOVE YOUR MOTHER, FRIEND, AVOID THIS ROAD.

THERE ARE WITCHES YONDER.

WITCHES, I TELL YOU.

SEE? THEY STOLE MY EARS WHILE I SLEPT, SO THAT I MUST WEAR MY HAIR LONG, FOR DECENCY'S SAKE...

CAN YOU SPEAK?

ah...YES, I...

WHAT HAPPENED?

I FEAR YOU HAVE BEEN *ATTACKED*, YOUNG MAN. THESE ROADS ARE NOT *SAFE* FOR INNOCENT TRAVELLERS, ALAS...

MY MONEY...

IT'S *GONE*.

A WORRY FOR *ANOTHER* DAY. FOR NOW, YOU NEED *FOOD*, AND *SLEEP*, AND *TREATMENT* FOR YOUR WOUND...

I *INSIST* THAT FOR TONIGHT AT LEAST, YOU SHALL ENJOY *MY* HOSPITALITY...

HYPATA, ESCORT THIS GENTLEMAN TO MY HOUSE, AND CATER TO HIS... NEEDS.

BUT I...

YOU *UNDERSTAND* ME?

YES. PERFECTLY.

COME, STRANGER. LEAN ON ME...

YOU'RE VERY KIND...

WHAT *GAME* IS THIS, TRIKALA? WE *NEED* FLESH, FOR THE RITES.

WHY DID WE NOT SIMPLY *TAKE* HIS FACE?

PATIENCE, BYRRHAENA....

I SMELL *STRANGENESS* ON THIS ONE, SOMETHING... NOT QUITE *MAN.*

SO *CHARM* IS NEEDED HERE, NOT FORCE. AND FOR *THAT,* SISTER, WE NEED YOUNGER *DUGS* THAN YOU OR I POSSESS.

Hee-hee...

SCRAWNY LITTLE THING THOUGH, ISN'T SHE?

IS SHE *UP* TO IT, D'YOU THINK?

OH, YES. OUR HYPATA HAS A STREAK OF *IRON* IN HER. AND IF YOU *CUT* HER...

I *SWEAR,* SHE WOULD BLEED *ICE.*

AND SO I FOLLOWED THE GIRL, OPEN-EYED, TO MY *DOOM*...

IS THE ROOM TO YOUR *LIKING,* STRANGER?

YES, INDEED...

AND-- *PLEASE*... CALL ME ARISTEAS.

THEN *TELL* ME, ARISTEAS...

...AM I TO YOUR *LIKING?*

GENTLE READERS, YOU MAY FIND THIS HARD TO CREDIT, BUT--SINCE I HAD HAD NO WISH TO *BUY* AFFECTION--IN ALL MY LONG MONTHS IN THE WORLD, THIS WAS MY *FIRST* VOYAGE ON THE *SHIP OF LOVE*...

AND THOUGH I HAD FORGOTTEN *THIS* ART ALSO, WITH WINE AND HYPATA'S TENDER ENCOURAGEMENTS, THE KNOWLEDGE RETURNED TO ME IN GOOD TIME...

AHHHHHHHHH...

THAT'S BETTER.

ROLL *OVER*, AND I WILL MASSAGE YOUR NECK...

WHERE ARE YOU *FROM*, ARISTEAS?

MARMORA...

MY NAME MEANS *NOTHING* TO YOU? ARISTEAS OF MARMORA?

NO. SHOULD IT?

MY VANITY THUS OFFENDED, I TOLD HER *EVERYTHING*: OF ARIMASPIA, OF MY DEPARTURE FROM EARTH AND MY CENTURIES OF SERVICE TO MY LORD, OF MY TRAVELS THESE LAST MONTHS...

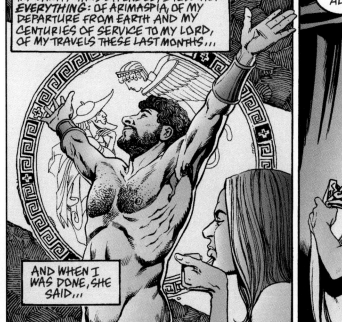

AND WHEN I WAS DONE, SHE SAID...

IS *THAT* ALL?

YOU PRATTLE OF *GODS* AND *GRYPHONS*...AND I THOUGHT YOU KNEW SOMETHING OF *VALUE*.

DO YOU THINK ME SOME IDIOT COUNTRY GIRL, TO BE *IMPRESSED* BY SUCH NONSENSE?

DIRE AS MY PREDICAMENT ALREADY SEEMED, IT NOW BECAME *WORSE...*

FOR NOT ONLY DID THESE DREADFUL WOMEN PRESS ME INTO SERVICE AS A BEAST OF BURDEN, BUT THE CARGO I WAS FORCED TO CARRY WAS GRISLY INDEED...

FASTER, O MESSENGER OF THE GODS.

NIGHTLY, I WAS COMPELLED TO WITNESS THEIR BLOOD-CURDLING RITUALS IN WORSHIP OF *HECATE,* THEIR DREAD MISTRESS...

...WHILE BY DAY THEY KEPT ME FIRMLY TETH-ERED, FED ON *ROTTEN* SCRAPS AND RAIN-WATER...

AND IN THIS PITIABLE CONDITION I REMAINED FOR SOME WEEKS, UNTIL I WAS RESCUED BY THE MOTHER OF MANKIND...

YOU *HAVE* GOT YOURSELF INTO A MUDDLE, HAVEN'T YOU?

COME ON, LET'S GET YOU *AWAY* FROM HERE...

...THE LADY *PANDORA* HERSELF.

IT'S LUCKY FOR *YOU* I HAD TO DELIVER A MESSAGE TO *CHIRON.*

HE *SAID* HE THOUGHT YOU WERE HEADING INTO TROUBLE...

...AND HE WAS *RIGHT,* WASN'T HE?

WELL, NEVER MIND...

HERE, EAT OF THESE ROSE PETALS, AND YOU SHALL SOON REGAIN YOUR *HUMAN* FORM...

THERE. *THAT'S* BETTER....

YOUR YEAR IS NEARLY *UP*, ARISTEAS.

HAVE YOU REACHED A DECISION YET ABOUT YOUR *FUTURE*?

YES... I HAVE.

I WANT TO BE A RAVEN AGAIN. I WANT TO GO *HOME*.

BUT *FIRST*...THERE'S A PLACE ON EARTH I WANTED TO *VISIT*, BUT...

MY *GOLD* WAS STOLEN, AND I HAVE NO *CLOTHES*...

SO I SEE. HERE...

LADY, COULD YOU *TAKE* ME THERE?

GRACIOUSLY, SHE CONSENTED, AND TRANSPORTED US BOTH TO THE CITY OF MY *DREAMS*...METAPONTION, IN OENOTRIA.

THE CLIMATE IS PLEASANT, THE FOOD AND WINE EXCELLENT, THE WOMEN COMELY, THE TOWN *YOUNG* AND *EXCITING*...

IF I COULD *DWELL* ANYWHERE ON EARTH, IT WOULD BE *HERE*.

BEAUTIFUL, ISN'T IT?

MY LORD BROUGHT ME HERE ONCE, *MANY* YEARS AGO, AND I HAVE NEVER FORGOTTEN IT.

BUT THAT KIND OF LIFE IS *BEHIND* ME...

...I KNOW THAT NOW.

STILL, I *WOULD* LIKE THE MAN I *WAS* TO BE *REMEMBERED*,...

...*HERE*, IF NOWHERE ELSE.

VERY WELL, THEN.

BUT IF WE'RE GOING TO PLAY OUT THIS LITTLE... *DRAMA* OF YOURS, YOU'D BETTER MAKE A *START*.

SO I ENTERED THE CITY'S MARKETPLACE, AND ADDRESSED THE *POPULACE*...

CITIZENS OF METAPONTION, *HEAR ME*...

I AM *ARISTEAS* OF *MARMORA*.

PISS OFF *BACK* THERE, THEN.

NEVER *HEARD* OF YOU.

I BEG YOU, *LISTEN* TO ME...

IT IS IMPORTANT THAT YOU KNOW THAT YOUR CITY IS *BLESSED*...

...FOR IT WAS ONCE VISITED BY,... A *GOD*.

WHICH GOD, *CURLY?*

YOU WOULD KNOW HIM AS *APOLLO*, THE FATHER OF *ORPHEUS*. I *ACCOMPANIED* HIM ON THAT VISIT, THOUGH I THEN *WORE* THE FORM OF A *RAVEN*.

AND IT IS *HIS* WISH THAT YOU BUILD AN *ALTAR* HERE TO HONOR HIM... AND BESIDE IT, A STATUE OF *MYSELF*.

BOLLOCKS.

221

WHAT HAPPENED NUH-*NEXT*?

DID THEY BUH-*BUILD* THE STUH-STATUE?

OH, YES...

OF COURSE, IT'S BEEN *DUST* FOR THE LAST THOUSAND YEARS OR SO...

POOR ARISTEAS. HE DID *SO* WANT TO BE IMMORTAL.

WHAT ABOUT HIS BUH-*BOOK*?

THE "ARIMASPEIA"? WELL, *WE* HAVE A COPY, BUT I DON'T THINK THERE'S BEEN ONE ON EARTH SINCE *ALEXANDRIA* BURNT DOWN.

STILL, LONGINUS QUOTES SIX LINES FROM IT IN HIS TREATISE ON GREAT WRITING... AND HERODOTUS GIVES ARISTEAS TWO WHOLE *PARAGRAPHS*...

I SUPPOSE THAT *IS* IMMORTALITY, OF A SORT.

WELL, HE SUH-CERTAINLY LIVED A LONG TUH-*TIME*.

I RUH-REMEMBER HIM BUH-BEING HERE FOR SUH-SUH-*CENTURIES* AFTER HE CAME BUH-*BACK*...

INDEED. QUITE A *FEW* CENTURIES.

THE TRUTH IS, HE WAS A *MUCH* BETTER RAVEN THAN HE WAS A MAN.

WUH-WHAT SORT OF A MUH-MAN WAS MUH-*MATTHEW*?